Wisconsin Puzzle Book

**By Donna Lugg Pape, Virginia Mueller
and Carol Karle**

**The Bess Press
P.O. Box 22388
Honolulu, HI 96822**

LEARN ABOUT WISCONSIN
THE FUN WAY

Our thanks to Alan Pape for his editing of Wisconsin material for the
Wisconsin Puzzle Book.

Cover Design: Roger Eggers
Typesetting and Design: Stats and Graphics

ISBN 0-935848-25-8
MANUFACTURED IN THE UNITED STATES
OF AMERICA

The State of Wisconsin

Identify the pictures in the rebus, then add or subtract letters as indicated to learn the date Wisconsin became the 30th state in the union.

Ethnic Match

Draw a line from the ethnic group named in the left column to something from their culture named in the right-hand column.

1. Ukranians
2. Mexican
3. Finnish
4. Swedish
5. Welsh
6. Scottish
7. Danish
8. Greeks

A. Kringle (a rich pastry)
B. Baklava (a rich pastry)
C. Pinata (paper mache shape)
D. Curling (a game played on ice)
E. Julbock (gingerbread in shape of a goat)
F. Exquisite embroidery work
G. Sauna (steam bath house)
H. Harp (national instrument)

Ethnic Match

Draw a line from the ethnic group named in the left column to something from their culture named in the right-hand column.

1. Swiss
2. Slovenian
3. Belgian
4. Cornish
5. German
6. French
7. Dutch
8. Norwegian
9. Irish

A. Aufwiederschen (a friendly farewell)
B. Shamrock (emblem with leaflets in groups of three)
C. Smorgasbord (variety of tasty foods)
D. Windmills with four wings
E. Fleur-de-lis (royal coat of arms)
F. Button box (a small accordion)
G. Maypole (high pole with streamers)
H. Wilhelm Tell (a hero in the fight for independence
I. Saffron buns (Saffron is a flavoring)

Chief Indian Tribes of Wisconsin

Rearrange groups of letters of each set to spell the name of Wisconsin Indian tribes.

1. WA MI TO PO TA __ __ __ __ __ __ __ __ __ __

2. PE IP CH WA __ __ __ __ __ __ __ __ __

3. WA TA OP __ __ __ __ __ __ __

4. TA DA KO __ __ __ __ __ __

5. O WI NN AG EB __ __ __ __ __ __ __ __ __ __

6. E ME MI NE NO __ __ __ __ __ __ __ __ __

7. OO AP CK KI __ __ __ __ __ __ __ __ __

8. WA IO __ __ __ __ __

Wisconsin Wildflowers

Unscramble the mixed up letters to spell common names of Wisconsin wildflowers.

1. R V L C O E _ _ _ _ _ _
2. S T I T H S E L _ _ _ _ _ _ _ _
3. P I N E U L _ _ _ _ _ _
4. L I O T E V _ _ _ _ _ _
5. M U L L I I R T _ _ _ _ _ _ _ _
6. T R O O D O O B L _ _ _ _ _ _ _ _ _
7. E I N C B M U O L _ _ _ _ _ _ _ _ _
8. Y R O C H I C _ _ _ _ _ _ _
9. Q N E E U N N S E A E C L A _ _ _ _ _ _

_ _ _ _ _ _ _ _ _ _

10. K C J A N I H T E P L U T I P

_ _ _ _ _ _ _ _ _ _ _ _ _ _

Which one is the state flower?

_ _ A = _

_ = N _ _ _

_ I =

_ = M _ _ _

_ _ A =

_ _ L =

_ _ _ _ _ _

Learn the name of Wisconsin's state ANIMAL by filling in the blanks next to each picture. When all the words are filled in, find the letters with the double line under them. Re-arrange these letters for the answer.

6

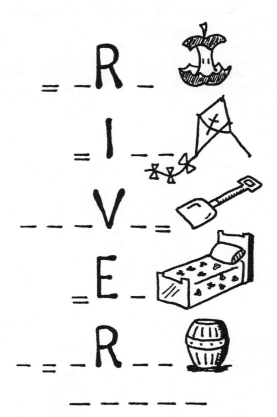

The highest waterfall in Wisconsin, Big Mani-tou Falls, is in Pattison State Park. The falls drop more than 165 feet. Find out what RIVER this falls is located on by filling in the blanks next to each picture. When all the words are filled in, find the letters with the double line under them. Rearrange these letters to find the answer.

7

Creative Wisconsin People

The first and last letters of given names and surnames are omitted in this list of creative Wisconsinites. Groups of the four needed letters for each name are listed. Letters are kept in proper order. Cross them off as you use them.

ADSR	GAOE
KLKS	ANBD
GECN	GYWT
JNCY	TRJN
HEGY	RHVK
EDSN	ATDH
HNGD	EAFR
LAWR	EAWX
BLNE	GEPK

1. __ALP__ __OTAPE__ - Pianist

2. __HO__ __ OHNSO__ - Conductor

3. __EORG__ __ATLL__ - Painter of Indian Portraits

4. __OH__ __ STEUART __ URR__ - Prizewinning Landscape Artist

5. __ARO__ __OHRO__ - Landscape Artist

6. __DWAR__ __TEICHE__ - Photographer

7. __LFRE__ __ESSLE__ - Graphic Artist

8. __DN__ __ERBE__ - Pulitzer Prize Winning Author
9. __ORAC__ __REGOR__ - Poet
10. __UGUS__ __ERLUT__ - Author
11. __AMLL__ __ARLAN__ - Pulitzer Prize Winning Author
12. __EORGI__ __'KEEFF__ - Artist
13. __AR__ __NATH__ - Abstract Artist
14. __LENWA__ __ESCOT__ - Novelist
15. __EORG__ __EC__ - Humorist
16. __IL__ __Y__ - Humorist
17. __LL__ __ WHEELER __ILCO__ - Poet
18. __AUR__ INGALS __ILDE__ - Author

9

Fact Maze

Begin with the W at the arrow and end with the starred R, finding the path through the maze. After finding the right path, copy the letters in the blanks to learn something about a product of the state.

W—I S—I—N—I—S—T—H
C—S N—S—I M—A—K E
O C—O—N H—E K I—N
N—S—L S T—N G—N G
D A N—I—N I O—F—T
A—E—L I O—N F E—H
D A I T—I I P L—E
S—T O A H—T A—P A
E H—E—N E—M—A E—R

_____ _____ ___

_____ __ ___ _____

__ _____

10

Hidden Trees

In each sentence below, the name of a tree found in Wisconsin is hidden. Underline the words as you find them.

1. Soda pop pleases most palates.
2. "How ill Owen seems," Mary said.
3. "Who is he?" M. Lockridge asked.
4. I told Mr. Spru centipedes have many legs.
5. Is one pin enough?
6. Mr. Wolf, I returned your scissors.
7. Pat Amar acknowledged the letter.
8. Once darkness frightened him.

Distributed throughout Wisconsin, the popple (quaking aspen) is the principal food of Wisconsin's large beaver population. They cut the trees down and eat their leaves, twigs, bud and inner bark. Deer, moose and rabbits eat the sprouts and ruffed grouse eat the winter buds of this species. Pioneers used its astringent bark as a quinine substitute.

= – **M** _

– **I** =

– **N** – – – =

– **E** – – = –

– = **R** – _

– = **A** =

L = – –

– – – – – – –

The mineral, dolomite, is found mainly in the southern part of Wisconsin. Another stone mineral is found on the central and northern sections. Find out the name of this MINERAL by filling in the blanks next to each picture. When all the words are filled in, find the letters with the double line under them. Rearrange these letters to find the answer.

F = _

= _ A _ _

_ R _ = _ _ _

_ _ M = _

_ I _ = _

_ _ N = _

_ = G _

— — — — — — — —

Wisconsin is a leading state in the production of green peas and sweet corn. Learn the name of another FARMING product from Wisconsin by filling in the blanks next to each picture. When all the words are filled in, find the letters with the double line under them. Rearrange these letters for the answer.

13

Spell the Fact

The alphabetized letter groups shown are the letters of an informative sentence in the proper order, but divided into groups of three. Place the groups in the correct order. Some letters are given as clues.

ASI	CTR	ELE	EIN	EWI
FIR	FOR	ICI	NAP	OUS
PLE	RED	STA	STH	TED
TES	THE	THE	TOB	TON
TYW	UNI			

_ _ _ _ _ _ _ _ _ _ _ U_ _ _ _

_ _ _ _ _ _ _ E_ _ _ _ _ _ _ _ _

_ _ _L_ _ _ _ _ _

_ _ _ _ _ _ _ _C_ _ _ _ _ _ _ _

_ _ _L_ _ _ _ .

14

Wisconsin Composers

The four people listed below have composed famous songs. Can you determine the names of these songs from the word listed and write each title next to its correct composer? First and last letters of titles are given.

BYE	VALE	SILVER	BALL
AND	SWEET	THE	BROWN
GOLD	AFTER	AMONG	IN
LITTLE	THE	IN	CHURCH
BYE	THREADS	THE	THE
THE			

1. Joseph Webster I _____ E
2. William Pitts T _____ E
3. Eben Rexford S_____ D
4. Charles Harris A _____ L

15

Mirror Image

When a picture is held up to a mirror, everything looks the same, but is reversed. However, in this mirror image of lumberjacks floating

logs down river to the sawmill during Wisconsin's logging boom in the 1860's, not everything is the same. Can you find the differences?

Fill A Space To Name A Place

This puzzle has two parts. First, fill in the middle three letters in Column A using clues in Column B. Then, using the pairs of letters shown below, fill in the first and fifth letters of each word. Three sets of first and fifth letters are given to help you. If you fill in the blanks correctly, the first and fifth letters reading down will reveal a special place at Delavan, Wisconsin.

Column A	Column B
_ _ _ _	Short for father
_ _ _ _	Abbreviation for Arizona
_ _ _ _	Abbreviation for United States
_ _ _ _	Abbreviation for North Carolina
_ _ _ _	Plural pronoun for ourselves
_ _ _ _	Opposite of off
_ _ _ _	Abbreviation for left end
_ _ _ _	Sixth note of the scale

OD   FA   HH   CR   OE   SR   OF   LE

Wisconsin "Firsts"

Each group of letters below spells a word belong in the Wisconsin, "Firsts" listed below. Unscramble the letters and place the words in their proper places.

STEA   TOEV   ISOL   TREWA
NOWEM   TELB   TEMMLUNPOYEN
LINGOWAL   STONEVORNICA
APOCTNESINOM

1. 1919 - Wisconsin is the first state to ap-
   prove law _ _ _ _ _ _ _ _
   _ _ _ _ _ to _ _ _ _.
2. 1932 - First state to pass an
   _ _ _ _ _ _ _ _ _ _ _ _
   _ _ _ _ _ _ _ _ _ _ _ _ law.
3. 1933 - First large _ _ _ _ and
   _ _ _ _ _
   _ _ _ _ _ _ _ _ _ _ _
   project in the United States.
4. 1961 - First state to pass a _ _ _ _
   _ _ _ _ law.

Fruits Of Wisconsin

Pardeeville calls itself "The City of Lakes" but it might as well be the City of _____. Pardeeville is the site of the annual United States _____ Eating and Seed-Spitting Championships.

Fill in missing letters of other fruits grown in Wisconsin. The correct letters will spell the fruit which made Pardeeville famous.

```
    S T R A _ B E R R I E S
        G R _ P E S
            _ O M A T O
  R A S P B _ R R I E S
        C H E _ R I E S
        P L U _ S
            P _ A R S
      A P P _ E S
        G O _ S E B E R R Y
        C R A _ B E R R Y
```

Find The Tree

Each row of letters includes the name of a tree found in Wisconsin, but one letter is missing. All the letters in each line will not be needed to spell the name of a Wisconsin tree. Draw a line around each tree after filling in the missing letter. If done correctly, the missing letters (reading down) will reveal the name of another tree.

```
W M O _ S Y C U P O A K X C B
D A Q _ A K I N G A S P E N F
C B I _ T O O T H A S P E N H
G D T _ M A R A C K B K M I T
I N O _ T H E R N R E D O A K
E H E _ L O C K K G L N T P E
Y S W _ M P W H I T E O A K S
V U R _ A P E R B I R C H F A
Z S I _ V E R M A P L E H J J
R I V _ R B I R C H O N Q X D
```

Flag Day

Read the paragraph below to learn some important facts about an event. Then search for the underlined words in the word-search puzzle. Circle the words starting in any direction. The leftover letters will spell the place and Wisconsin city where this event began 94 years ago.

School teacher Bernard Cigrand got the idea of honoring June 14 as the birthday of the American flag. It was on that date in 1777 that Congress officially adopted the Stars and Stripes.

```
B E R N A R D S T O N
S T A R S I D E A Y H
E N U J I L L R S C H
P N A C I R E M A O O
I L H S O H U S E 1 4
R W A U C I G R A N D
T B Y A D H T R I B G
S S E R G N O C E K A
E T A D E T P O D A L
H O N O R I N G L A F
```

First And Last Letter Find

In 1946, Sheboygan became the first city in the state and the third in the United States to conduct certain testing led by Dr. Almore Finke. To learn what this was, use the pairs of letters below to fill in the first and last letters missing in the list of words. The answer will appear as you read the letters down.

IT   RG   AO   LT   OO   AD   EI   OA
FH   TE   UT   DH   NY   WT
IC   TF   RO

```
_ U R S _
_ U D I _
_ H I E _
_ N V O _
_ U I N _
_ R E S _
_ I G H _
_ P S E _
_ U T G _
_ A D I _
_ N E P _
_ U T C _
_ V O I _
_ H E M _
_ O N I _
_ P E R _
_ O B L _
```

23

Bird Words

Take one of the letters listed below and by exchanging it with a letter in Column A form a new word in Column B. Do not rearrange the letters to form the new word. Then, take the letter you have removed and place it in Column C. Rearrange the letters in Column C to form a related term.

L F A L H P B R L O C

Column A	Column B	Column C
TERN	_ _ _ _	_ _
DOVE	_ _ _ _	_ _
KITE	_ _ _ _	_ _
PHEASANT	_ _ _ _ _ _ _ _	_ _
WREN	_ _ _ _	_ _
CRANE	_ _ _ _ _	_ _
EIDER	_ _ _ _ _	_ _
SWANS	_ _ _ _ _	_ _
RAIL	_ _ _ _	_ _
COOT	_ _ _ _	_ _
BAIRD	_ _ _ _ _	_ _

(Type of Sparrow)

A Wisconsin bird not named above is the Bobolink. Many of them migrate as far as Argentina to spend the winter. Much of their traveling is done at night.

24

Name Match – What Is It?

Draw a line from the name in the left column to the correct answer in the right-hand column.

1. Kaolinite
2. White Heel Splitter
3. Namekagon
4. Avoca
5. Menominees
6. Lucius Woods
7. Mendota
8. Black Jack

A. Pine Tree
B. State Park
C. Type of stone used by Indians for peace pipes
D. Name of a Wisconsin prairie
E. Inland Lake
F. Wild River
G. Fresh water mussel
H. Ethnic group

Indian peace pipes were carved from a stone that hardens as it dries.

Wisconsin has eight wild rivers. They are designated as wild rivers because of scenic natural surroundings and white water.

There are known to be 23 varieties of fresh water mussels in the Mississippi River. They were formerly harvested for their shells for the pearl button industry.

This ethnic group has their own county (the 72nd in Wisconsin), their own government, and their own industry.

This pine tree (Jack Pine) produces seed that remains viable for 20 years. The cones open best in the heat of a fire and is, therefore, an uncertain process.

Learn which Wisconsin town was named after
a game played by the early Indians of that area
by filling in the blanks next to each picture. The
letters on the lines below the arrow, when read
down, will spell out the answer.

Find out the name of Wisconsin's state flower by filling in the blanks next to each picture. The letters on the lines below the arrow, when read down, will reveal the answer.

27

Find a Fact

Fill each group of letters in the proper place in the puzzle grid. Some clues are given.

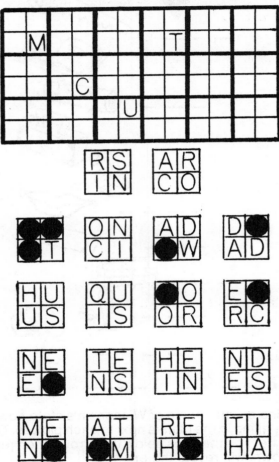

Leftover Letters

Spell out ERICH WEISS by drawing a line in any direction a letter at a time. Leftover letters will give the well-known name of this Wisconsin man.

E H C O
R I U H
D I W E
S S I N
I

DIOUINH

Make a Match

Match the names of places in the first column to the correct word in the column on the right.

1. Rib D
2. Sullivan G
3. Horicon F
4. Apostle A
5. Lac Du Flambeau C
6. Green Bay E
7. St. Croix River B

A. Islands
B. River
C. Indian Reservation
D. Mountain
E. Bay
F. Marsh
G. Waterfall

29

- APS +

- P + - T +Y

+ $\frac{2}{CUPS}$ - P +

- B + - P

+ - F + R =

_ _ _ _ _ _ - _ _ _

_ _ _ _ _ _ _ _ _ _ _ _

Wisconsin's first newspaper was started in 1833. Identify the pictures in this rebus and add or subtract letters as indicated to find out its name.

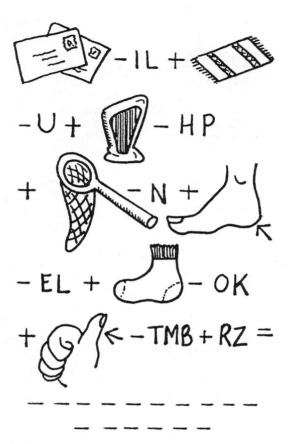

The first kindergarten in America was begun at Watertown, Wisconsin, in 1856 by a German woman who came to live in the United States. Learn her name by identifying the pictures in this rebus and adding or subtracting letters as indicated.

Mystery Lake

Each row of letters contains the name of a lake found in Wisconsin, but with one letter missing. All the letters in each row will not be needed to form the word. Draw a line around each lake, filling in the missing letter. If correct, the letters reading down will spell the name of another lake, Next start with the top row and go from left to right, copying down your unused letters in the blanks. Some information about the mystery lake will be revealed.

```
L  A  R  G  E  S  _  O  N  G  T  O
F  O  P  O  Y  G  _  N  V  E  R  E
I  G  H  P  U  C  _  A  W  A  Y  T
Y  F  B  U  T  T  _  R  N  U  T  I
C  H  I  P  P  E  _  A  V  E  H  U
N  D  R  E  S  P  _  D  E  R  D  L
A  K  E  S  M  E  _  D  O  T  A  W
H  I  C  H  G  E  _  E  V  A  A  R
E  M  A  P  G  R  _  E  N  P  E  D
I  N  T  H  E  S  _  A  L  S  A  M
T  A  C  H  E  T  _  C  T  E  O  F
W  I  S  C  E  A  _  L  E  O  N  S
I  K  O  S  H  K  _  N  I  N  G  N
```

_ _ _ _ _ _ _ _ _ _ _

_ _ _ _ _ _ _ _ _ _ _ _ _ _

_ _ _ _ _ _ _ _ _ _ _

_ _ _ _ _ _ _ _ _ _ _ _ _ _

_ _ _ _ _ _ _ _ _ .

Place the Letters

To learn some information about an event that took place in Wisconsin in 1878, fill in each blank square with one of the given letters in its column. Some letters are given to help you get started.

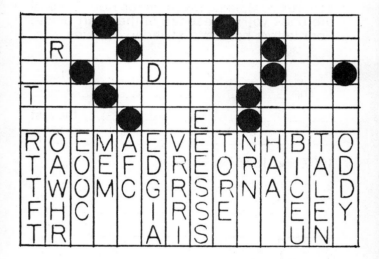

Wisconsin Sports History

The missing words in the two Wisconsin sports facts can be determined by working the tricky puzzle on the opposite page. The puzzle words are represented by numbers, with each number standing for a different alphabet letter. When you determine the letter that matches a certain number, put the letter into all the squares containing that number. Keep track of the ones you've decoded in the chart below. Four letters have been filled in as clues.

1. The_ _ _ _ _ _   _ _ _ _   _ _ _ _ _ _ _ _

_ _ _ _ _ _ _ _ _ _   _ _ _ _ _   _ _ _ _ the first

_ _ _ _   _ _ _ _ _ _   _ _ _ _   _ _ _ _ in

1967 and 1968.

2. In 1957, the _ _ _ _ _ _ _ _ _ _

_ _ _ _ _ _ _   _ _ _ _ _ _ _ _ _

_ _ _ _ _   _ _ _ _ the _ _ _ _ _ _

_ _ _ _ _ _ _ .

1.__	5.__	10.__	15.__	19.__
2.__	6.__	11.__	16.__	20.__
3.__	7.__	12.__	17.__	21.__
4.__	8.__	13.__	18.__	

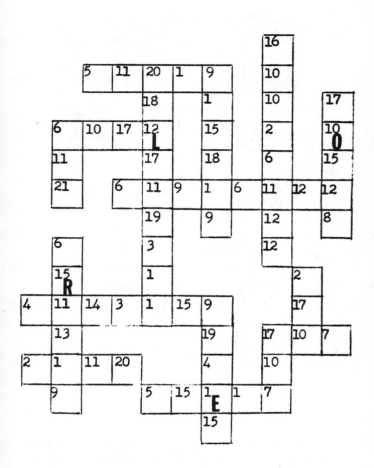

35

_ _ _ _ _ _

_ _ _ _ _   _ _ _ _ _ _

To learn the name of an important Wisconsin city and why it is important, identify the pictures in this rebus and add or subtract letters as indicated.

$-TO + O +$

$-O +$  $-AR + U$

$+$ $-OS +$

$-MT +$  $-BG =$

_ _ _ _ _ _ _

_ _ _ _ _ _

Who started a trading post on the east bank of the Milwaukee River in the area that was later to become Milwaukee, Wisconsin's largest city? Learn the name of this man, who has been called the "Father of Milwaukee" by identifying the pictures in this rebus and adding or subtracting letters as indicated.

37

Place the Consonants

Only the vowels are given in the fact below. To reveal the information, use one consonant or group of consonants to complete each word. Cross off consonants in the list as you use them.

S	TH	RD	FRST	MDSN	PRTNG
T	BY	WS	STTN	STTN	PPRCTN
N	TH	TH	LDST	FRST	BRDCST
WH	RD	WH	STTN	DCTNL	CNTNSLY
RD	TH	MSC	WRLD	PRGRM	

_ _e o_ _e_ _ _o_ _i_uou_ _ _

o_e_a_i_ _ _a_io _ _a_io_ i_

_ _e _o_ _ _ i_ _a_io _ _a_io_

_ _A a_ _a_i_o_. _ _e _i_ _ _

_u_i_ a_ _e_ia_io_ _ _o_ _a

_a_ _ _oa_ _a_ _ _ _ _ _ _A,

_ _e _i_ _ _ e_u_a_io_a_ _a_io

_ _a_io_ .

38

Find a Fact

Place the words from the sentence in the fill-in puzzle. Then transfer the numbered letters to the corresponding numbered blanks in the sentence to learn the missing words.

The Eagle River chain of

$\overline{}_{1}$ $\overline{}_{2}$ $\overline{}_{3}$ $\overline{}_{4}$ $\overline{}_{5}$ $\overline{}_{6}$ - $\overline{}_{7}$ $\overline{}_{8}$ $\overline{}_{9}$ $\overline{}_{10}$ $\overline{}_{11}$

lakes is thought to be the very largest fresh-water lake chain in the world.

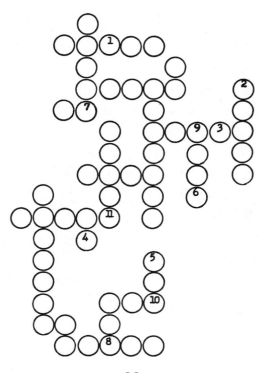

39

Unusual Museums

Wisconsin has some unusual museums. Each group of letters and blanks provides information about a Wisconsin museum. Vowels need to be inserted and words must be separated.

1. Th_ M_s_ _m _f M_d_c_l Pr_gr_ss _t Pr_ _r_ _ d_ Ch_ _n _xh_ib_ts d_p_ct m_d_c_n_'s pr_gr_ss _n W_sc_ns_n _nd th_ M_dw_st.

2. Th_ N_t_ _n_l R_ _lr_ _d M_s_ _m _t Gr_ _n B_y pr_s_rv_es th_ h_st_ry _f r_ _lr_ _d_ng.

3. Th_ D_rd H_nt_r P_p_r M_s_ _m _t _ppl_t_n d_spl_ys th_ h_st_ory _f p_p_r-m_k_ng m_th_ds.

4. Th_ c_ _ntry's m_st c_mpl_te c_ll_ct_on _f g_ns c_n b_ s_ _n _n M_d_s_n _t th_ m_s_ _m _f th_ St_t_ H_st_r_c_l S_c_ _ty _f W_sc_ns_n.

5. _xh_b_ts _f h_st_r_c _gr_c_lt_r_ _ m_ch_n_ry _nd _ _rly h_ndcr_fts c_n b_ s_ _n _t th_ St_t_ F_rm _nd Cr_ft M_s_ _m _n N_ls_n D_w_y St_te P_rk.

6. Rh_n_l_nd_r's L_gg_ng M_s_ _m h_s _n_ _f th_ m_st c_mpl_t_ d_spl_ys _f _ld-t_m_ L_mb_r_ng.

7. Th_ C_rc_s W_rld M_s_ _m _t B_r_b_ _ d_spl_ys _bj_cts r_c_ll_ng d_ys wh_n W_sc_ns_n w_s th_ L_ _d_ng c_rc_s st_t_.

41

Wordy Wheel

For information about a sports personality, begin with the top row of letters at the starred F, copying down every third letter going clock-wise three times. Repeat the procedure with the second circle of letters, beginning with the C in the starred wedge, this time going counterclock-wise as you copy every third letter. Continue in the same manner alternating between clockwise and counterclockwise until you have copied all of the letters. Use the blanks below.

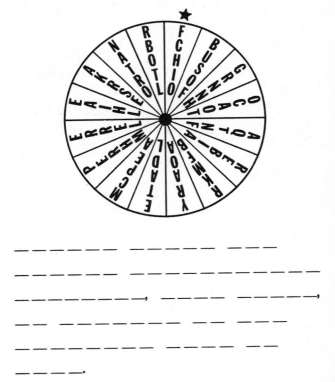

_ _ _ _ _ _ _   _ _ _ _ _   _ _ _

_ _ _ _ _   _ _ _ _ _ _ _ _ _

_ _ _ _ _ _ _ _ ,   _ _ _ _   _ _ _ _ _ ,

_ _   _ _ _ _ _ _ _   _ _   _ _ _

_ _ _ _ _ _ _   _ _ _ _   _ _

_ _ _ _ .

Wisconsin Military Heroes

To learn the missing names from these facts about military heroes, use the letters below each fact to make three letter words.

1. Lt. Col. Joseph __ __ __ __ __ __ , an engineer, saved a Union fleet during the Civil War.

I B A Y E L __ __ __ __ __ __
      I C V O Y E
      N E Y W E S

2. Richard __ __ __ __ __ __ __ shot down forty Japanese planes during World War II.

G R I N A O B __ __ __ __ __ __ __
       N O P U W E N
       K B T Y N W U

3. The __ __ __ __ __ __ __ __ brothers, Alonzo, Howard, and William, were Civil war heroes. William sunk the Confederate ship, Albemarle.

N U G H I S C __ __ __ __ __ __ __ __
        D S L E M E U
        G E Y X P T M

Make a Match

Rock formations of the Wisconsin Dells are world famous. Match the words in the first column to the correct words in the second column for names given to these cliffs and rocky formations.

1. Sugar	A. Dark Waters
2. Hawk's	B. Gulch
3. Grand	C. Rock
4. Cave of	D. Yards
5. Witch's	E. Bowl
6. Fat Man's	F. Elbow
7. Stand	G. Bill
8. Devil's	H. Arrowhead
9. Navy	I. Misery
10. Giant	J. Piano

Find a Fact

Place the words from the sentence below in the fill-in puzzle. Then transfer the numbered letters to the corresponding numbered blanks in the sentence to reveal the missing word.

Some of the first _ _ _ _ _ _ _ _ utensils
              1 2 3 4 5 6 7 8
ever manufactured were produced in the state of Wisconsin.

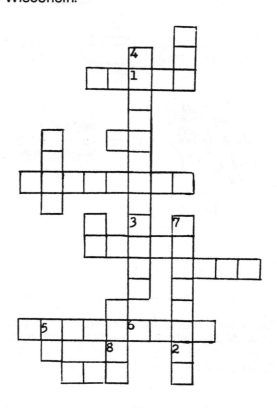

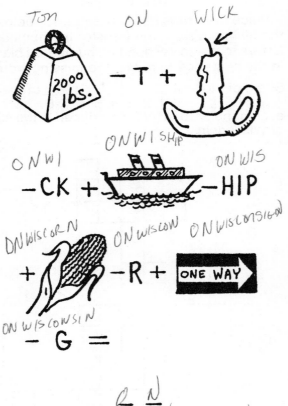

Ton *ON* *WICK*

$-T + $

ONWISHIP

ONWI *ONWIS*

$-CK + $ $-HIP$

ONWISCORN *ONWISCON* *ONWISCONSIGN*

$+ $ $-R + $ ONE WAY →

ONWISCONSIN

$- G = $

W I S C O N S I N
(with R N above CO·N·)

Wisconsin's motto is "Forward." Find out the name of the state song by identifying the pictures in this rebus and adding or subtracting letters as indicated.

46

U

T

T

O

R

$\underline{I}\ \underline{R}\ \underline{O}\ \underline{U}\ \underline{T}$

Learn the name of one of the many fish caught in Wisconsin waters. Identify the pictures, write down the first letter of each one, then rearrange these letters and write the answer on the lines provided.

Minerals in Wisconsin

In each square, you'll see two letters. Cross out a letter in each square so your leftover letters spell the names of minerals found in Wisconsin. Words should read across and down.

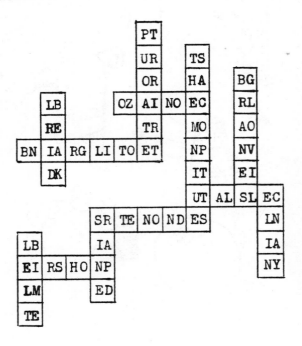

Plant the Rows

Transfer the vertical rows of letters to the correct rows in the grid and you'll learn an agricultural fact.

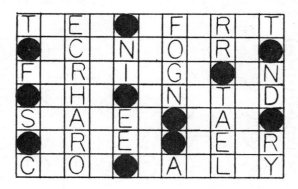

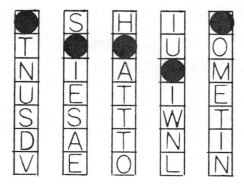

Fact Maze

To learn something about the Lac du Flambeau area, begin with the I at the arrow and end with the starred D, finding the path through the maze. After finding the right path, copy the letters in the blanks.

↓

```
I  T  H  A   H  E  M  O  S
T  S  A  S   T  A  F  O  T
I  S  I  M   O  N  E  G  I
N  O  D  T   R  E  R  O  O
E  E  B  O   E  K  E  I  N
O  T  E  B   F  A  T  N  K
F  H  E  R   D  L  H  O  N
T  E  M  O   E  T  E  W  O
H  R  T  S   T  A  W  O  R
B  T  C  T   A  R  T  R  L
E  S  O  N   C  E  N  T  D ★
```

__ __ ____ __ __ ___

____ _____

____ _____ __ ___

_____.

Name Find

Use the letters given below to make three letter words. If correct, you will be able to fill in the following sentence:

__ __ __ __ __   __ __ __ __, at age 70, became the first woman Prime Minister of Israel.

```
        R  L  E  G  M  D  I  O  A
              ____ EL
              ____ AK
              ____ EG
              ____ IN
              ____ ND
              ____ IX
              ____ LK
              ____ NN
              ____ YE
```

Mirror Image

When a picture is held up to a mirror, everything looks the same, but is reversed. However, in this mirror image not everything is the same. Can you find the differences in these pictures of

Frenchman Jean Nicolet who was dressed in an oriental outfit when he greeted Wisconsin Indians in 1634 because he thought he had found a route to China and would be meeting the Chinese Emperor?

Wisconsin's Largest Waterfalls

Each row of letters contains the name of one of Wisconsin's largest waterfalls, but with one letter missing. The missing letters reading down spell the name of Wisconsin's sixth largest waterfall. Draw a line around each waterfall, filling in the missing letter. Next start with the top row and go from left to right, copying down your unused letters in the blanks. Some information pertaining to large Wisconsin waterfalls will be revealed.

F O U R _ A X O N O F T H

E M A R _ N N A M E D E F

O U C O _ P E R N D I N T

H G I L _ E M O N T R E A

L R M O _ G A N I V E R I

N I R B _ G M A N I T O U

O N B R _ W N S T O N E C

P O W E _ D A M O U N T Y

_ _ _ _   _ _   _ _ _ _   _ _ _

_ _ _ _ _   _ _   _ _ _

_ _ _ _ _ _ _ _   _ _ _ _ _   _ _

_ _ _ _   _ _ _ _ _ _ .

54

Weather Word Fill In and Name Find

In Wisconsin there are sudden and extreme changes of temperature; winters are generally cold and summers are warm. Using the words listed below, complete this fill-in. Then transfer the letters in the numbered squares to the corresponding numbered blanks below to provide the missing name.

Autumn, Hot, Hail, Sleet, Rain, Snow, Cold, Windy, Warm, Humid, Winter, Spring, Blizzard, Summer.

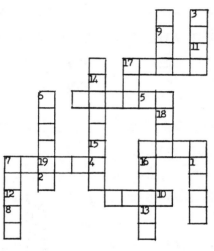

$\overline{1}$ $\overline{2}$ $\overline{3}$ $\overline{4}$ $\overline{5}$ $\overline{6}$ $\overline{7}$ $\overline{8}$ $\overline{9}$ $\overline{10}$ $\overline{11}$ $\overline{12}$ $\overline{13}$

$\overline{14}$ $\overline{15}$ $\overline{16}$ $\overline{17}$ $\overline{18}$ $\overline{19}$

a Wisconsin scientist, was called the father of the United States Weather Bureau. He was responsible for the establishment of a United States Weather Bureau.

Wisconsin Inventors

Place the words listed in the appropriate blanks to learn some information about these Wisconsin inventors.

OR EN HOT FIR SEE ROLL EASE

IN IN PEW WIN HIT SCAT RITE

MA EN FIN OUR WIT QUIP FULL

HI US PRO APE BIND CALL PROVE

ME HER ATE ION AUTO VENT ELOPE

MI BUN MEN BIN RAIN LONG GRAPH

CHIN

1. George Van Brunt in_ _ _ _ed the
_ _ _st ma_ _ _ _e to _ _ _ _ter
and bury _ _ _ds success_ _ _ _y.
2. John Stevens dev_ _ _ _ _d a
_ _ _ _er _ _ll to incr_ _ _ _ _
_ _ _duct_ _ _ of _ _ _e, w_ _ _e
fl_ _ _.
3. John Appleby _ _v_ _ted a t_ _ _e
_ _ _ _er _ _c_ _ne f_ _ _ _e on
re_ _ _rs to _ _ _d _ _ _dies of
g_ _ _ _ _ _ _ _mati_ _ _ _y.

4. Both Peter Houston, Jr. and Henry Bennett
cre_ _ _d and im_ _ _ _ _d
p_ _ _o_ _ _ _ _ _y e_ _ _ _ _ _ _t.
5. Christopher Latham Sholes a_ _ _ _
_ _ _h two ot_ _ _ _ _n, _ _v_ _ted
the ty_ _ _ _ _ _ _ _r.

Leftover Letters

To learn of a popular tourist attraction in the southwestern part of Wisconsin near Spring Green, spell out SPRING GREEN by drawing a line in any direction a letter at a time. Copy down the leftover letters in order.

```
S   T   H   I   E   H   O
U   P   R   S   N   E   O
N   T   H   E   E   G   E
R   O   N   C   K   R   G
```

Word-Chain

In this word-chain, some information is hidden. Words are connected end to end in the diagram. Pencil in the path from word to word. The numbers under the lines below give you each word length. The RACINE is given as the beginning of the sentence.

```
N A T O D S L P F E D N X
M T G H C N E U A B O O B
D H I A J H C L D I A F N
O G N V T A A B T L F P A
I U H E L R G A B M E H N
R O K S G J L C I O S A C
A H M E B U H B P I G E E
L T S G P E D L N U B T S
S T F O S O E A C N E L T
L I P B K F D T Q I H B R
D R E N I C A R X T T M Y
P P E V M L K P M E A N I
L Y R S E T A T S D H R B
```

_____ __ _____
__ ____ __ _____
_____ __ _____
__ _____ _____
__ ___ _____ _____.

58

Lower the Letters

In 1832 the Black Hawk War took place which ended the power of Indians in Wisconsin. To learn the name of the last fight in the war, read each clue and write the answer in the circles following the numbers. Then place each circled letter in the square directly below it at the bottom of the grid.

1. Robert M. LaFollette was known as "Fighting ___ ___ ___."

2. Pattison St__ __ __ Park is in northwest Wisconsin.

3. Chief Black Hawk ___ ___ ___ the Sauk Indians in the war.

4. In 1911, the first state income ___ ___ ___ was adopted.

5. Manitou __ __lls is Wisconsin's highest.

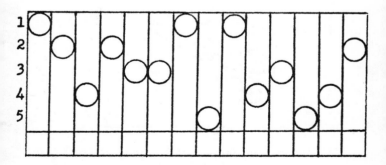

_ _ _ _ _

What large, web-footed birds spend part of the year at Wisconsin's Horicon Marsh? Identify the pictures, write down the first letter of each one, then rearrange these letters to learn the answer.

‒ ‒ ‒ ‒   ‒ ‒ ‒ ‒ ‒

‒ ‒ ‒ ‒ ‒

‒ ‒ ‒ ‒ ‒

What architect, born in Richland Center, was known for his "prairie style" designed homes and for such future plans as his 1 mile high skyscraper? Learn his name and the name of his home in Spring Green by identifying the pictures in this rebus, and adding or subtracting letters as indicated.

City Match-up

Match the cities in the first column to their correct descriptions in the second column.

1. Kenosha

2. Fish Creek

3. Oconto

4. Ashland

5. Waukesha

6. Ripon

7. Manitowoc

8. Superior

9. Sturgeon Bay

10. Monroe

11. Elkhart Lake

A. Location of the world's largest cherry orchard.

B. Noted for fine mineral water from springs.

C. The Republican Party was formed here in 1854.

D. Home of the largest manufacturer of aluminum ware in the world.

E. Site of Road America International Auto Racing Sports Center.

F. First Christian Science Church ever built was constructed here in 1886.

G. Place where the first house by a white Wisconsin settler was built.

H. International headquarters for the Society for the Preservation and Encouragement of Barber Shop Quartet Singing in America.

I. Famous summer theater and music festival is held here each year.

J. Site of the tallest grain elevator.

K. Known as the Swiss Cheese Center of America.

Wisconsin Counties

Each county below has a pair of letters missing. From the group of letter pairs, fill in the correct letters, crossing off the pair as you use it.

TT PP EE FF NN RR SS OO

D_OO_R
BA_RR_ON
LaCRO_SS_E
BURNE_TT_
DU_NN_
BU_FF_ALO
CHI_PP_EWA
GR_EE_N

A Governor Remembered

All of the vowels have been omitted from this word search puzzle. The puzzle contains the words from the following sentence. Look for these words and fill in the vowels.

ROBERT MARION LA FOLLETTE WAS THE FIRST NATIVE-BORN WISCONSIN GOVERNOR.

After you have filled in the vowels and circled the words in the above sentence, find four other occupations of Robert LaFollette. Vowels have been omitted from the named occupations. Remember, words can go forward, backward, up, down and diagonally.

```
L  _  W  Y  _  R  R  W  B
_  R  M  T  S  _  W  _  G
F  R  _  J  H  F  R  S  N
_  _  M  M  F  _  T  C  X
L  N  B  _  R  Y  D  _  T
L  R  M  _  R  _  D  N  R
_  _  T  S  R  _  F  S  _
T  V  W  H  P  N  _  _  B
T  _  _  V  _  T  _  N  _
_  G  T  _  A  C  H  _  R
Z  C  R  _  T  _  N  _  S
```

Winding River Search

The names of these rivers in Wisconsin wind. Some wind more than others. Draw a line around them. You may go in any direction.

BARABOO	OCONTO
CHIPPEWA	PESHTIGO
FLAMBEAU	SHEBOYGAN
KICKAPOO	TREMPEALEAU
MANITOWOC	WISCONSIN
MENOMINEE	YELLOW
NAMEKAGON	PIGEON
MULLET	NEMADJI

```
E C M A L F C S I W D O
A R A B G R K O W H B T
M B Q X E N I S N E O N
L F O S B A V C H I Y O
L E V O L W U S O T G C
U K T J H T I G D A O E
M E N A N S M A N I L N
O C O I Z E E L N T S R
O Y M P E K E P O O Q A
P H S M I K I G W M U G
C A A C O J A O E P A Y
H N K I B D C R P E E E
I J N E M A T F I A L L
P P E W A N O E G W O L
```

Unscramble the Boxes

Write the correct words to match the definitions on the numbered dashes. Then transfer
your letters to their corresponding numbered
boxes. The letters over number 1 will go in Box 1,
a letter over a 2 will go in Box 2 and so forth. Then
unscramble the letters in each box to reveal
some agricultural information.

1. Animals found on dairy farms.

$$\overline{}\ \overline{}\ \overline{}\ \overline{}$$
$$\ \ 3\ \ \ 9\ \ \ 11\ \ 4$$

2. Opposite of fat

$$\overline{}\ \overline{}\ \overline{}\ \overline{}$$
$$\ \ 2\ \ \ 7\ \ \ 11\ \ 8$$

3. A stick or switch

$$\overline{}\ \overline{}\ \overline{}$$
$$\ \ 2\ \ \ 3\ \ \ 7$$

4. Sojourn

$$\overline{}\ \overline{}\ \overline{}\ \overline{}\ \overline{}$$
$$\ \ 7\ \ \ 4\ \ \ 9\ \ \ 12\ \ 7$$

5. Unsettled area

$$\overline{}\ \overline{}\ \overline{}\ \overline{}\ \overline{}\ \overline{}\ \overline{}\ \overline{}\ \overline{}\ \overline{}$$
$$\ \ 9\ \ \ 2\ \ \ 11\ \ 4\ \ \ 6\ \ \ 3\ \ \ 9\ \ \ 12\ \ 7\ \ \ 2$$

6. A creature with fins

$$\overline{}\ \overline{}\ \overline{}\ \overline{}$$
$$\ \ 2\ \ \ 9\ \ \ 10\ \ 1$$

7. A group of Indians having the same habits

$$\overline{}\ \overline{}\ \overline{}\ \overline{}\ \overline{}$$
$$\ \ 1\ \ \ 7\ \ \ 9\ \ \ 6\ \ \ 7$$

8. Worn on the head

$$\overline{}\ \overline{}\ \overline{}$$
$$\ \ 9\ \ \ 4\ \ \ 3$$

9. Barterers

$\overline{5}\ \overline{12}\ \overline{7}\ \overline{11}\ \overline{7}\ \overline{12}\ \overline{9}$

10. Narrow light boat

$\overline{12}\ \overline{10}\ \overline{9}\ \overline{5}\ \overline{1}$

11. Wisconsin (Abbr.)

$\overline{10}\ \overline{8}$

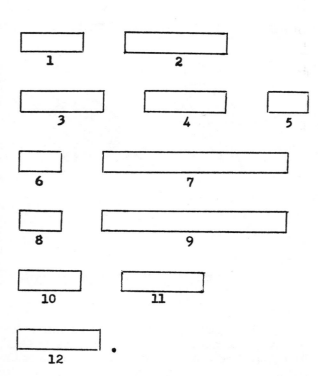

Part of the folklore of Wisconsin includes stories about a giant lumberjack and his special friend. To find out their names fill in the blanks below each picture. The letters above the double lines will reveal the answer.

= – = – =   = = – = –

– – = – = = –   = – = –

– = = –   – = =

– – – –   – – – –

– – – –   – – – –

69

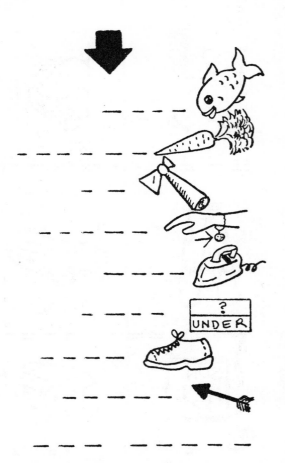

The first hydroelectric plant in the nation was built in 1882 in a Wisconsin town. Find out where it was built and in what city by filling in the blanks next to each picture. The letters on the lines below the arrow, when read down, will reveal the answer.

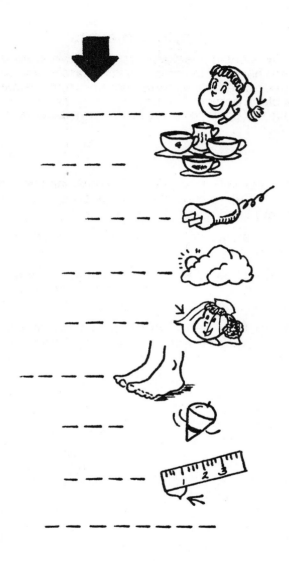

Black Achievers

Wisconsin has many black achievers; people who have left their mark in important ways. Each group of letters below provides information about a black person. The letters are in correct order, but the spacing is wrong. Write the sentences correctly.

1. Ezek ialG il lispi efo ug hta ndwo nint heW isc onsi nSup re meCo urtt her ightf orb la ckst ovo teinW is co nsin.

2. AlJ ar eaui saf amo ussi nge ran dreco din gst ar.

3. Bla ckda nc er,F ern eCau lk-erB rons on, fo unde dth eKo -ThiD an ceCom pa nyw hi chpe rfo rms th rough out th emi dw est.

4. In1 978, Ba rba raN ic hols,b eca met hefir stbla ck tob eel ect edp re side nto ft heAm erica nNur se'sA sso ci at ion.

Spell The Fact

The alphabetized 3-letter groups are the letters of an informative sentence. Rearrange them to form a fact about a Wisconsin haven for rare and endangered birds. Less than 3 letters indicates a sentence ending. Some letters are filled in to get you started.

ANE   ANE   ARA   ARB   ATI BOO COL
ERN   FOU   GES   HAS   INT LAR LCR
LDS   LEC   N. NDA NNE ONA TCR
THE   THE   TIO   TIO WOR.

_ _ _ _ _ _ _ R _ _ _ _ _ _ _ _ _

_ _ _ _ _ _ _ _ _ D _ _ _ _ _

_ _ _ _ _ _ _ _ _ _ _ _ _ _

_ _ _ _ _ _ _ _ _ _ _ _ _ _ _ _ _

C _ _ _ _ _ _ _ _ _ _ _ _ _ _ _ _ .

Define, Delete, Discover

Fill in the answers to the definitions of all the words in Column A. Then, fill in the answers to all the words in Column B. Cancel out the letters from the Column B words that appear in the Column A words. Write the remaining letters, in order, in the spaces provided. The answer will be the name of a group of restored Cornish miners' homes in Mineral Point, Wisconsin.

Column A Clues:

1. Abbreviation for puppy — — —

2. Years from 13 through 19 — — — —

3. Opposite of very untidy — — — —

4. To fall in drops — — — —

5. Common Wisconsin mineral found at Mineral Point — — — —

6. To rip into shreds — — — —

7. To wander — — — —

8. Water falling to earth — — — —

9. A place or space to sit — — — —

Column B Clues:

1. Opposite of down   __ __
2. A cardinal number   __ __ __
3. To take nourishment   __ __ __
4. To tear   __ __ __
5. Homonym of 5A   __ __ __
6. A common drink   __ __ __
7. Fish eggs   __ __ __
8. Past tense of run   __ __ __
9. To put food into the mouth   __ __ __

__ __ __ __ __ __ __ __ __

Wisconsin Nicknames

Match the nickname in the right hand column to its true name.

1. Kame   A. Sodbuster

2. Woodcock   B. Upside down Kettle

3. Squirrel   C. Winnebagos Cod

4. Rabbit   D. Bushytails

5. Chinook Salmon   E. Skunk Spruce

6. Wisconsin
   Glacier   F. Drummers

7. Muskrat   G. Cottontail

8. White Spruce   H. Marsh hare

9. Male Grouse   I. Ice Giant

10. Burbot   J. King

11. Plow   K. Timber Doodles

Follow The Directions

This Wisconsin city's name means Gathering Place by the Waters.

1. Print the letters of the meaning without any spaces between the letters.

GATHERINGPLACE
BYTHEWATER

2. Eliminate all consonants
3. Reading from left to right replace last 2 vowels with vowels not represented
4. An important Wisconsin product is M I L K Add the letters to spell this word before and after a vowel in the string of vowels.
5. There are three alike letters. Eliminate the first one of the three (left to right)
6. Find the letter that describes yourself and move it to the left two spaces.
7. Replace the first letter of the alphabet (also first in the string of letters) with the 23rd letter of the alphabet
8. Eliminate a letter that describes an exclamation
9. Unscramble to spell a thriving Wisconsin metropolitan city and the answer to this puzzle

_ _ _ _ _

To learn the name of Wisconsin's state bird, identify the pictures, write down the first letter of each one, then rearrange these letters to get the answer.

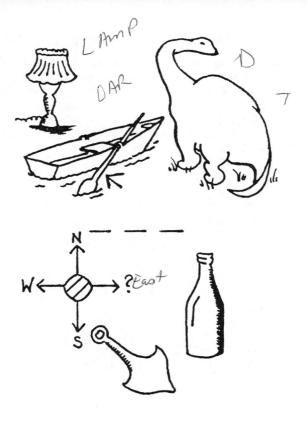

During the Civil War, a Wisconsin regiment had an eagle for a mascot. He even joined the soldiers in battle. After the war, he lived in the State Capitol. To learn his name, identify the pictures, write down the first letter of each one, then rearrange these letters and write the answer on the lines provided.

A Woman Remembered

A Wisconsin woman's name will be revealed if you find your way through the maze correctly. Start with the F at the arrow and end with the starred letter D. Copy the name you discover in the blanks below. Next fill in the vowels in the words of the sentences to learn something about this person.

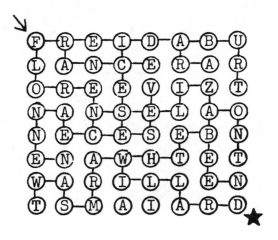

__ __ __ __ __ __ __   __ __ __ __ __ __ __ __

__ __ __ __ __ __ __

f__ __nd_d th__ W_rld's W_m_n's

T_mp_r_anc_ _n_ _n. _ft_r h_r

d__th _n 1898, a st_t__ _f h_r w_s

pl_c_d _n th_ H_ll _f F_m_ _t th_

C_p_t_l _n W_sh_ngt_n.

80

Word Fill-in

Use the words listed below to fill in the missing parts to learn some information about Wisconsin.

IN	TO	AS	BAD	USE	TEA
HO	HE	ON	HAT	MAD	ATE
OR	TI	HE	NOW	LEA	KING
SO	HE	AD	TAT	ERR	MINE
ID	WE	HI	ALL	ROW	
BE	HE	ON	NOR	ILL	

Wisconsin is _one_e of t_he_ six s_tat_es
w_hi_ch _hav_e up w_ _ _ _ w_ _ _ _ _ce
k_ _ _n as t_ _ _ _ _ _th_ _st
t_ _ _it_ _y. Wisconsin is c_ _ _ _ed t_ _
_ _ _ger st_ _ _ _ _ca_ _ _ _ _ _me of
t_ _ _ _ _ _d _ _ _ _ _rs bur_ _ _ _ ed
in_ _ s_ _es of h_ _ _ _s like b_ _gers
_ _s_ _ _d of ta_ _ _ _ _ _ _me to
build _ _uses.

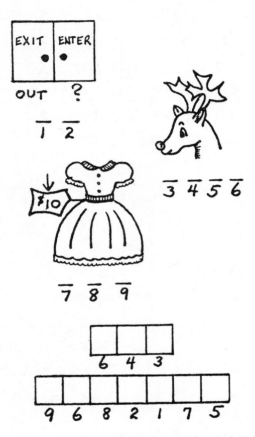

EXIT | ENTER

OUT   ?

$\overline{} \ \overline{}$
$1 \quad 2$

$\overline{} \ \overline{} \ \overline{} \ \overline{}$
$3 \quad 4 \quad 5 \quad 6$

$10

$\overline{} \ \overline{} \ \overline{}$
$7 \quad 8 \quad 9$

6	4	3

9	6	8	2	1	7	5

To learn the name of Wisconsin's state stone, fill in the blanks under each picture. Then transfer the letters into the matching numbered boxes.

A Creative Woman

To learn the name of a Wisconsin woman, start with the top letter at the arrow. Go around the circle clockwise three times, copying every third top letter in the blanks next to number 1. Then go back to the arrow. Start with the bottom letter. Go around the circle clockwise again, three times, copying every third bottom letter in the blanks next to number 2.

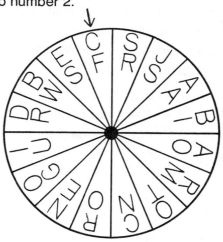

1. _ _ _ _ _ _ _ _ _ _ _ _ _ _ _ _ _

2. _ _ _ _ _ _ _ _ _ _ _ _ _ _ _ _ _

Sentence Deciphering

Each group of letters provides information about medical history being made in Wisconsin. The letters are in correct order, but the spacing is wrong. Write the sentences correctly.

1. Dr.Wi lli amBe aum ontm ad eimp ort antd isc ov erie scon ce rnin gdi gesti onoff ood.

2. Wi scon sinsc ient ist, Dr.H ar ryS t eenb ockcon duc teda nex peri men tw hi chle dt oth edis co very tha tult ravi ole tra diati onprod uc esvi ta minD info ods.

3. Dr.El merVM cCol lumd is co ver edVitami nsA,B, an dDwh iled oingr es ear chatt heU niver si tyofW is consi nin Ma dison.H ewa sassi sted byMar gu eri teDa vis.

Maze and Fact Find

The middle of this puzzle contains a maze. Start at the starred W and work your way through the maze until you reach the starred D. The correct path will spell a Wisconsin man's name. Write the names in the blanks provided below. Next start at the H in the upper left corner. Going clockwise three times, copy down every third letter in the blanks to reveal information about the man.

↓

H	T	D	E	H	E	I	E	R	S	F
O										N
E										K
G		* Ⓦ Ⓐ Ⓛ Ⓣ Ⓔ Ⓡ							A
M		Ⓘ Ⓛ Ⓡ Ⓓ Ⓡ Ⓘ							D
B		Ⓛ Ⓛ Ⓐ Ⓝ Ⓓ Ⓒ							N
N		Ⓛ Ⓘ Ⓐ Ⓞ Ⓐ Ⓗ							T
F		Ⓘ Ⓢ Ⓜ Ⓗ Ⓡ Ⓓ *						A
O										O
I	O	T	Y	R	N	R	E	W	I	H

Name __ __ __ __ __ __ __ __ __ __ __ __ __ __ __

__ __ __ __ __ __ __ __ __ __ __ __ __ __ __ __ __ __ __

__ __ __ __ __ __ __ __ __ __ __ __ __ __ __.

85

Word Search Discovery

Read the paragraph below to learn some important facts about a State Historical attraction at Eagle, Wisconsin. Leftover letters briefly describe this place. Circle the underlined words in the word search puzzle.

<u>Old</u> <u>World</u> <u>Wisconsin</u> is the only <u>multinational</u>, multicultural <u>outdoor</u> <u>museum</u> in the world. Assembled here are more than <u>forty</u> buildings originally constructed by the <u>immigrant</u> settlers who came to Wisconsin during the <u>nineteenth</u> century. Already the <u>Danes</u>, <u>Finns</u>, <u>Germans</u>, <u>Norwegians</u>, <u>Swiss</u>, and <u>Yankees</u> are represented. Eventually, over one hundred buildings will represent sixteen <u>ethnic</u> groups.

```
O  L  A  N  O  I  T  A  N  U
M  U  E  S  U  M  T  I  I  D
S  F  O  R  T  Y  S  S  N  O
N  I  O  R  D  N  W  E  E  C
A  N  E  T  O  H  I  E  T  I
I  N  N  C  O  I  S  K  E  N
G  S  S  C  R  M  S  N  E  H
E  I  M  M  I  G  R  A  N  T
W  T  D  U  S  E  D  Y  T  E
R  L  A  U  M  E  A  L  H  G
O  U  N  L  E  D  L  R  O  W
N  M  E  G  E  R  M  A  N  S
```

Fill A Space To Name A Place

This puzzle has two parts. First, fill in the middle three letters in Column A using clues in Column B. Then, using the pairs of letters shown below, fill in the first and fifth letters of each word. Three sets of first and fifth letters are given to help you. If you fill in the blanks correctly, the first and fifth letters reading down will reveal a special place in Wisconsin.

Column A   Column B

__ __ __ __ __   1. Tiny

__ __ __ __ __   2. To take nourishment

__ __ __ __ __   3. Past participle of light

__ __ __ __ __   4. Form of "have"

__ __ __ __ __   5. To flog

V   U

E   N

O   D

__ __ __ __ __   6. First part of a major
                               California city
                               (Spanish name)

FS   TT   CM   HH   AO   EE

Follow The Directions

John Michael Kohler, who founded the Kohler Plumbingware Company at Kohler, Wisconsin, was a boy of ten when he came to this country in 1873. The Waelderhaus was dedicated to his memory by his daughter, Marie Christine Kohler.

Follow the directions carefully to find what this name means.

1. Copy the letters in The Waelderhaus without spaces between. We have done this for you to get you started.
   THEWAELDERHAUS

2. The last four letters is a German word meaning house. Eliminate the German word and write the English spelling.

3. Move the letter representing the first vowel in the alphabet so that it is first in the string of letters.

4. Remove the letters that name an occupation.

5. Reading from left to right, move the second, third, and fourth letters so that they are the 7th, 8th and 9th letters.

6. Add the letters in the word WISCONSIN after the second E from the left.

7. Working from right to left move the last two letters to a spot between house and the.

8. Reading from right to left remove letters that spell abbreviation for sister.

9. Remove the letters used to abbreviate the state of North Carolina.

10. Add the letters that stand for the word "help" to the right of the letter that is first from the right or last from the left.

11. Working from left to right move the third "O" in the string of letters to a spot next to the second "O" in the string of letters.

12. Change the abbreviation for a baseball term to an abbreviation for Doctor of Science.

Fraction Action

This city in Wisconsin is the home of the first Dutch language paper in the United States (issued in 1849).

3/5 of SHELL	___
	___
	___
1/2	___
	___
1/3 of YES	___
1/4 of FLAG	___
2/3 of FAN	___
	___

= = - - = - = =

= = = = - - = =

- - = = = - - - - = =
- - - - - - - =
- - - -

Fill in the blanks below each picture. The letters above the double lines will spell out the name of the state wildlife animal of Wisconsin.

Learn the name of Wisconsin's state tree by filling in the blanks below each picture. The letters above the double lines spell out the answer.

Wisconsin Sports Stars

Match the word parts from the first column to the correct part in the second column. Then use the words to fill in the missing words in the sentences about sports stars on the opposite page.

1. HIT	A. CHER
2. OLYM	B. TING
3. PACK	C. CHES
4. RE	D. IZED
5. COA	E. SIDERED
6. ME	F. GLE
7. PIT	G. BALL
8. CON	H. ING
9. SIN	I. BALL'S
10. CHAM	J. TER
11. GREAT	K. ERS
12. SKA	L. CORD
13. ORGAN	M. DALS
14. BASE	N. EST
15. HOLD	O. PICS
16. FOOT	P. PION

Wisconsin Sports Stars

1. Sheila Young Ochowicz is the first American
   to win three _ _ _ _ _ _ in speed
   _ _ _ _ _ _ _ _ in a _ _ _ _ _ _
   Winter O L Y M P I C S.

2. Denton (Cy) Young, _ _ _ _ _ _ _ _ the
   _ _ _ _ _ _ for the most games won by a
   _ _ _ _ _ _ _ _, is in _ _ _ _ _ _ _ _ _ '_
   Hall of Fame.

3. _ _ _ _ _ _ _ _ _ _ home run _ _ _ _ _ _ _ _,
   Hank Aaron, played most of his _ _ _ _ _ _ _
   in Milwaukee.

4. Earl Louis Lambeau _ _ _ _ _ _ _ _ _ _
   the Green Bay P A C K E R S
   F O O T B A L L team.

5. Vince Lombardi was _ _ _ _ _ _ _ _ _ _ _
   one of the _ _ _ _ _ _ _ _ _ of football
   _ _ _ _ _ _ _ _.

Place The Consonants

Only the vowels are given in the information below. To reveal the information, use one consonant to complete each word. Cross off consonants in the list as you use them.

D	ST	CRT	FLMB
N	LC	CRX	WSCNSN
R	ML	RVR	RSRVTNS
ND	BD	NDN	STCKBRDG
LC	LK	RLLS	MNMN

__ _. _ _oi_ _, _a_ _ou_ _

O_ei_ _e_, _a_ _u _ _a_ _eau,

_o_e _a_e, _e_o_i_ee,

_ _o_ _ _ _i_ _e, a_ _ _a_ _i_e_

a_e L_ _ia_ _e_e_ _a_io_ _ _ i_

_i_ _o_ _i_ .

94

Make A Word

Match the word parts from the first column to the correct parts in the second and third columns. Then use the words to fill in the missing words in the sentences.

RE	TLE	DENTS
NA	ING	TON
WASH	LAN	DIC
SET	TION	AL
ICE	SI	MENT

1. _ _ _ _ _ _ _ _ _ _ Island has the

   largest _ _ _ _ _ _ _ _ _ _ of

   _ _ _ _ _ _ _ _ _ of

   _ _ _ _ _ _ _ _ _ descent in the United

   States.

2. The St. Croix and Lower St. Croix rivers are

   _ _ _ _ _ _ _ _ rivers.

Word Pie

This word pie is divided into 6 pieces. Each piece, except one, has a letter. Determine which letter starts the last name of one of Wisconsin's latest explorers. Also fill in the missing letter.

James A. _ _ _ _ _ _

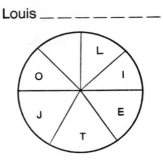

This word pie is divided into 7 pieces. Each piece, except one, has a letter. Determine which letter starts the last name of a Canadian trader, explorer and mapmaker who was given the task of seeking a route to the Pacific by way of the Mississippi River. Also fill in the missing letter.

Louis _ _ _ _ _ _ _

This word pie is divided into 9 pieces. Each piece, except one, has a letter. Determine which letter starts the last name of a French missionary and explorer. He was the first European to cross Wisconsin.

Jacques _ _ _ _ _ _ _ _ _

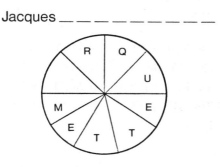

Wisconsin Detective

Can you find
1. A bench from a church in CHIPPEWA
2. An ordinal number in SIOUX
3. A word for yourself in MENOMINEE
4. A vegetable in POTAWATOMI
5. An animal in SAUK
6. A container in WINNEBAGO
7. A beast of burden in FOX

All of the capitalized words are names of Wisconsin Indian tribes. Indians were Wisconsin's first residents.

Place The Consonants

Only the vowels are given in the fact below. To reveal the information, use one consonant or group of consonants to complete each word. Cross off consonants in the list as you use them.

B TH PRK STT   DVLPD   WSCNSNS
S ND STT PRK   TGTHR   STBLSHD
S TW PRK WHCH MNNST   FRST
T TH STT FRST WSCNSNSTTS
VR BY PRK WRKNG NTRSTT

__i__o__i_'_ __i___ __a_e

__a__ i_ L_e___a_e __a_e

__a__. _o__i_ _o_e__e_,

__i__o__i a__ __i__e_o_a

e__a__i_e_ __e _a__

___i__ i_ ___e __i___ __a_e

__a__ e_e_ _o _e _e_e_o_e_

__ ___o ___a_e_.

98

Dot Detective

Start with the first row and go from top to bottom, copying down every letter to the left of the dots. Place the letters in the blanks provided below to learn something that took place at Baraboo in 1884.

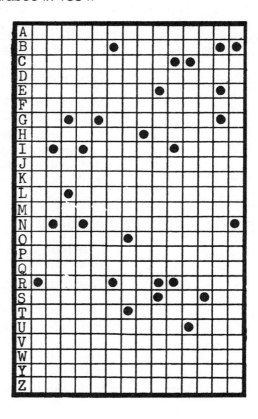

_ _ _ _ _ _ _ _   _ _ _ _ _ _ _ _

_ _ _ _ _ _   _ _ _ _ _.

99

Madeline Island

The Madeline Island Historical Museum is located on the largest of the Apostle Islands off the northernmost tip of Wisconsin. These twenty-two offshore islands are part of the Apostle Islands National Lakeshore Area created by Congress in 1969 to preserve the stunning beauty of lakeshore, sky, and water.

Complete the spelling of these Islands of Wisconsin by filling in the answers to the clues.

1. B_ _ _   Organ of hearing

2. _ _ _ _ _Y   Mass of stone forming a peak or cliff

3. _ _ _ _ _ _   Furry, flesh-eating mammal related to weasel and mink with webbed feet

4. _ _ _ITOU   A human being

5. STOCK_ _ _   2,000#

6. _ _ _   Tree that grows from an acorn

7. _ _ _ _   Disintegrated rock

8. _ _ _ _ _ _   National emblem of the U.S.

9. _ _RK   One-half of the name of a spoollike toy

10. _ _ _ _ _BERRY   A rough file

11. _ _ _ _ _WOOD   Metallic chemical element that can be magnetized

100

12. _ _ _ _ _ _ Another name for Satan (possessive form)

13. _ _ _ A feline

14. _ _ _ _ Common water bird

15. _ _ _ER Opposite of in

16. _ _ _MIT Opposite of Him

17. _ _ _ _WOOD Common Wisconsin fish

18. _ _POINTE Sixth note of the musical scale

19. _ _ _ _ Opposite of short

20. _ _ _ _ _ _ _ _ _ Name of the Great Lake that borders on the east

21. SOUTH_ _ _ _ Forming a pair of look-alikes

22. NORTH_ _ _ _ Forming a pair of look-alikes

Wisconsin Riddles

1. How would you address a letter to the river that forms the western boundary of Wisconsin?

2. What large inland lake in Wisconsin is like a contest for a hard bread roll? (Largest freshwater lake within the contiguous 48 states; 215 square miles)

3. What city in Wisconsin needs mending? (Home of the Republican party)

4. What could a Wisconsin resident get from his neighbor state?

5. What did the suitor say to his girlfriend named Claire? This city has a French name meaning clear water.

6. There are several Wisconsin cities whose beginnings you use when you don't know the words of a song. What are they? These cities begin with a French word meaning "the".

Chair

Legs

Dress

Flag

WING

Ladle

Charles
De Langlade

The man who has been called the "Father of Wisconsin" was born in Mackinac and lived with the Ottawa Indians as a boy. Learn his name by filling in the blanks below each picture. The letters above the double lines will spell out the answer.

Word Search Discovery

Read the paragraph below to learn some important facts about a State Historical attraction at Greenbush, Wisconsin. Leftover letters briefly describe this place.

<u>Old</u> <u>Wade</u> <u>House</u> is located near the northern tip of the <u>beautiful</u> <u>Kettle</u> <u>Moraine</u> State Forest in the village of <u>Greenbush</u>. Wade House offered welcome respite to weary <u>travelers</u>. Todays visitors find Wade House, the <u>Charles</u> <u>Robinson</u> house, and Sylvanus Wade's <u>blacksmith</u> <u>shop</u> restored to appear as they did 125 years ago.

```
H  T  I  M  S  K  C  A  L  B  B
S  K  T  A  G  E  C  O  H  E  E
S  E  L  R  A  H  C  S  A  N  A
C  T  D  L  O  H  U  H  I  I  U
N  T  N  O  N  B  T  O  H  A  T
E  L  W  I  N  S  I  P  C  R  I
O  E  N  E  S  I  N  N  F  O  F
R  O  E  N  T  I  E  R  S  M  U
T  R  A  V  E  L  E  R  S  O  L
G  E  S  U  O  H  E  D  A  W  N
```

Mystery Word Puzzle

By placing the words from the headline below in the appropriate spaces, two mystery words will appear in the circles.

Complete the puzzle and then fill in the mystery words.

Headline dated 1888: Julius Schemmel, Wisconsin, patents his inventive snow vehicle.

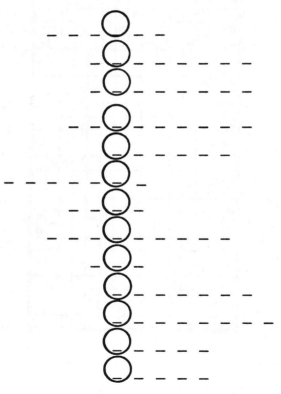

Dot Detective

Many show business personalities have been Wisconsin residents. For information about Spencer Tracy and Frederic March, start with the first row and go from top to bottom, copying down every letter to the left of the dots. Place the letters in the blanks provided below.

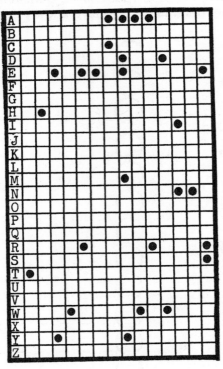

_ _ _ _   _ _ _ _ _   _ _ _ _ _ _ _ _

_ _ _ _ _   _ _ _ _ _ _ _ _ .

Gone From The Skies

To learn the name of birds that nested in Wisconsin in large numbers but who are now gone from the skies, go around the circle clockwise and copy every third and write the letters in the blanks in the paragraph below the circle.

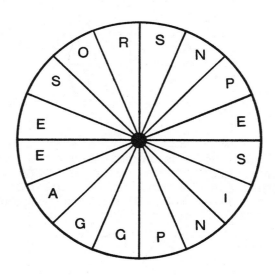

One Indian chief told the famous naturalist, John Muir: "I saw one nesting place in Wisconsin 100 miles long and from three to ten miles wide."

A monument to _ _ _ _ _ _ _ _ _ _

_ _ _ _ _ _ _ _ can be seen by travelers along the ridges of Wyalusing State Park near Prairie du Chien.

Word Pie

This word pie is divided into 8 pieces. Each piece has a letter, except one. Determine which letter starts the name (first) of an explorer and map maker who traveled through Wisconsin in 1766. Also fill in the missing letter.

J O N A T H O N Carver

This word pie is divided into 6 pieces. Each piece, except one, has a letter. Determine which letter starts the first name of a French explorer fur trader who explored in Northwestern Wisconsin. Also fill in the missing letter.

D A N I E L Duluth

This word pie is divided into just 4 pieces. Each piece, except one, has a letter. Determine which letter starts the first name of the first European to see Wisconsin. He landed at Red Banks on Green Bay in 1634. Also fill in the missing letter.

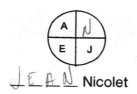

J E A N Nicolet

Round Up

Each of the letter-circles below represents a word that can be spelled out by starting at the correct starting letter and moving clockwise around the circle. You may use letters over again, but you may not skip over a letter. All of these words are something you would find in nature in Wisconsin.

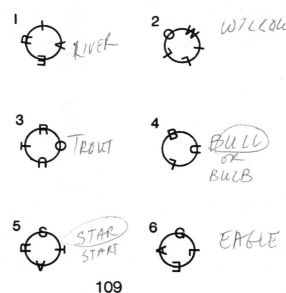

1. RIVER

2. WILLOW

3. TROUT

4. BULL or BULB

5. STAR START

6. EAGLE

109

Mystery Words Puzzle

By placing the words from the sentence below in the appropriate spaces, two mystery words will appear in the circles.

Complete the puzzle and then fill in the mystery words.

__ __ __ __ __ __ __ __ __ __ __ with Experi-mental Aircraft Association and Air Museum hosts the worlds largest fly-in convention.

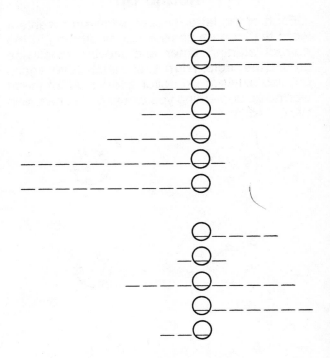

Wisconsin Word Search

By going up, down, forwards, backwards, and even diagonally find the following words in the word search grid. Leftover letters will title this puzzle.

```
W  H  I  F  O  R  E  S  T
P  R  I  S  C  G  O  S  S
R  E  N  L  R  S  F  E  L
A  E  N  O  L  F  S  L  L
I  F  G  I  I  E  E  T  A
R  S  I  L  N  N  E  T  F
I  E  C  U  T  S  L  E  R
E  K  D  A  S  O  U  K  E
M  A  P  G  V  O  O  L  T
A  L  O  G  R  E  C  A  A
K  B  P  M  A  R  S  H  W
V  A  L  L  E  Y  S  H  Y
```

WISCONSIN
TOPOGRAPHY

HILL	REEFS	MARSH
LAKES	DUNES	VALLEYS
LEES	GORGE	FOREST
BOGS	CLIFFS	PRAIRIE
KAME	COULEES	PENINSULA
CAVES	KETTLES	WATERFALLS

111

Fill A Space To Name A Place

This puzzle has two parts. First, fill in the middle three letters in Column A using clues in Column B. Then, using the pairs of letters shown below, fill in the first and fifth letters of each word. Three sets of first and fifth letters are given to help you. If you fill in the blanks correctly, the first and fifth letters reading down will reveal a special place at Janesville, Wisconsin.

Column A		Column B
_ _ _ _ _		To impair
_ _ _ _ _		Abbreviation for Russian
_ _ _ _ _		Common suffix
O	B	
O	L	
L	I	
_ _ _ _ _		Short form of Rio de Janeiro
_ _ _ _ _		Nickname for Ronald

ON   ST   FD   HE   CH

Father Rene Menard, the first missionary to the Wisconsin Indians, arrived about 1660. A Wisconsin town, county, and university are named after another missionary who came to the area after Menard. Learn his name by filling in the blanks below each picture. The letters above the double lines will spell out the name.

113

Adopt An Animal Fillin

Listed below are a few of the animals in the Adopt an Animal program. Place their names in the fill-in puzzle. Then unscramble the circled letters and you will be able to complete the following sentence:

"The _ _ _ _ _ _ _ _ _   _ _ _ _ _ _

_ _ _   is one of the best in the world."

APE	OWL	SKINKS
EEL	BOAS	CHEETAH
ELK	LION	GAZELLE
YAK	CAMEL	HORNBILL

FLAMINGO	COPPERHEADS
WALLAROO	HIPPOPOTAMUS
ALLIGATOR	EASTERN MILK SNAKE
FIREMOUTH	SEAL

115

Wisconsin Fish

The Wild Rose State Fish Hatchery produced more than one-half million trout. Three of the answers to this puzzle are names of trout found in Wisconsin waters. Find the eight other fish; if done correctly, the name of another fish will appear.

```
S  A  L  _  O  N
   S  T  _  R  G  E  O  N
   B  A  _  S
   P  I  _  E
      P  _  R  C  H
      _  A  K  E   (name of a Wisconsin
                          trout)
      B  _  U  E  G  I  L  L
      S  _  C  K  E  R  S
R  A  I  _  B  O  W   (name of a Wisconsin
                              trout)
   T  I  _  E  R   (name of a
                    Wisconsin trout)
   S  M  _  L  T
```

$$\underline{}\ \underline{}\ \underline{N}\ \underline{}$$
$$1\quad 2\quad 3\quad 4$$

$$\underline{S}\ \underline{E}\ \underline{A}\ \underline{L}$$
$$5\quad 6\quad 7\quad 8$$

(V, ?, X, Y)
$$\underline{W}$$
$$9$$

N	E	W
3	6	9

	L	A			S
4	8	7	1	2	5

To learn the name of a village in the southern part of Wisconsin which is the home of many people of Swiss descent, fill in the blanks under each picture. Then transfer the letters into the matching numbered boxes.

117

Dot Detective

John Muir became known as one of America's greatest naturalists. To learn another title given to John Muir, start with the first row and go from top to bottom, copying down every letter to the left of the dots. Place the letters in the blanks provided below.

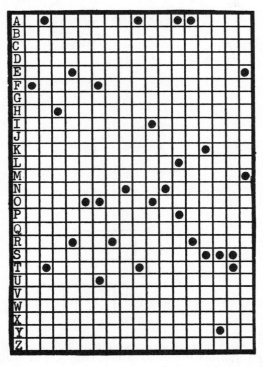

_ _ _ _ _ _ _ _ _ _ _ _

_ _ _ _ _ _ _ _ / _ _ _ _ _

_ _ _ _ _ _ .

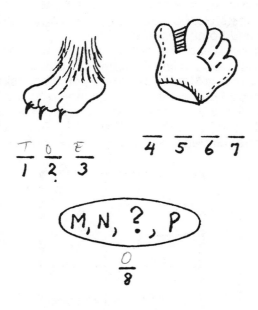

$$\frac{T}{1} \quad \frac{O}{2} \quad \frac{E}{3}$$

$$\overline{4} \; \overline{5} \; \overline{6} \; \overline{7}$$

M, N, ?, P

$$\frac{O}{8}$$

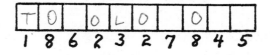

T	O		O	L	O		O		
1	8	6	2	3	2	7	8	4	5

Many Indian tribes have lived in Wisconsin. Some were the Sauk, the Winnebago and the Menominee. To learn the name of the Indians who camped in the area that is now Door County, fill in the blanks under each picture. Then transfer the letters into the matching numbered boxes.

Bottom To Top
Top To Bottom Puzzle

Fill in the four-letter answers in the numbered columns. For some you will work from the bottom up and some from the top down.

Then, read the letters across the top and bottom rows to find the name of a place operated by The State Historical Society of Wisconsin. The circled letters will be unscrambled to spell the name of Wisconsin's first governor. This historical attraction is named after his 2,000 acre farm. (Letter circled twice is used more than once)

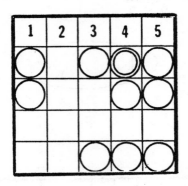

CLUES:

1. Person in feudal servitude
2. Short form of taxicab
3. Man-eating monster in fairy tales
4. Mown grass
5. To observe

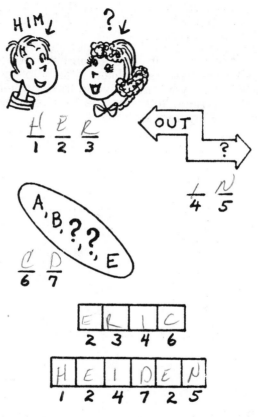

HIM↓   ?↓

$\underset{1}{H}\ \underset{2}{E}\ \underset{3}{R}$

OUT   ?

$\underset{4}{I}\ \underset{5}{N}$

A, B, ?, ?, E

$\underset{6}{C}\ \underset{7}{D}$

E	R	I	C
2	3	4	6

H	E	I	D	E	N
1	2	4	7	2	5

What Wisconsin person won 5 gold medals in skating events at the 1980 Winter Olympic Games in Lake Placid, New York? To find out, fill in the blanks under each picture. Then transfer the letters into the matching numbered boxes.

121

Mystery Statement

Words in this puzzle are represented by numbers. Each number stands for a different letter of the alphabet. After you figure out the letter that matches a certain number, put the letter into each square containing that number. Also fill in the letter chart with letters you have decoded. Four letters have been filled in to help you get started. After you have filled in the words in the puzzle, arrange them on the blanks below to reveal the mystery statement.

1 -	11 -
2 -	12 -
3 - A	13 -
4 -	14 - N
5 -	15 -
6 -	16 - R
7 -	17 -
8 -	18 -
9 -	19 -
10 - T	

_ _ _ _ _ _ _ _   _ _ _ _ _ _   _ _ _

_ _ _ _   _ _ _ _ _ _   _ _   _ _ _ _ _ _

_ _ _ _ _ _ _ _ _ _   _ _ _ _ _ _

_ _ _ _   _ _ _   _ _ _ _ _

_ _ _ _   _ _   _ _ _   _ _ _ _ _ _

_ _ _ _ _ _ .

Spell To Tell

Choose a letter from each group of letters to spell the names of mammals found in Wisconsin now or at one time. (Those marked with an asterisk are now extinct or near extinction.) The names will read across with one letter missing from each name which you must provide. Cross off letters as you use them and write the names in the spaces. Another animal's name will appear in the circles. Now copy down the unused letters in order in the spaces beneath the mammals named to learn something about the "mystery animal".

```
*   TI  !T  MI  SB  EB  RE  __  LO  IL  FE

                        SV  __  RE  DE  WW  IS

        SR  CA  OB  BN  __  ST

                    IB  NA  __  IS

    SS  QH  OU  SI  RT  TR  __  LO

*               AM  TA  LR  __  EE  AN

*               PS  UT  MF  __

*                   IF  __  SV  HE  EH  RU

*       BN  DU  FR  FE  AD  __  OT

*               HM  OO  LU  __

                SB  AA  __  GN  DE  OR

                    __  EF  TE  HR

*       WI  SO  ML  AV  __  RM  IM  NA  EL

*                   __  AL  NK

*               CN  UA  __  IA  BL  LO  UY
```

124

Wisconsin Wealth Word Search

By going up, down, backwards, forwards, or diagonally, find products that contribute to the Wisconsin economy. There are 15.

```
M C A K O P R S C L
F L N J L H E E A U
E O S Y C I B L T M
S V G E R S M P T B
E E G R E T U P L E
E R E L T A L A E R
H H A Y T O G U I K
C O R N U Q S G O H
D B T O B A C C O P
```

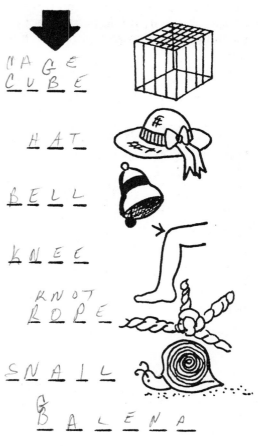

C A G E
C U B E

H A T

B E L L

K N E E

K N O T
R O P E

S N A I L

G
B A L E N A

In 1971, Wisconsin named what mineral as its state mineral? Find out by filling in the blanks next to each picture. The letters on the lines below the arrow, when read down, will spell out the answer.

Nature Color Matchup

Draw a line from the color to the words in the right hand column. If you do this correctly, it will be the name of something in nature found in Wisconsin.

1. Brown   A. Bunting

2. Black   B. Lovegrass (a prairie grass)

3. Blue   C. Perch

4. Purple   D. Pelican

5. Gold   E. Bear

6. Yellow   F. Gill

7. White   G. Trout

8. Red   H. Oak

9. Scarlet   I. Finch

10. Indigo   J. Tanagers

White _ _ _ _ _ _ _ _ are not common in Wisconsin but a few show up every year.

= — —   — = = =

— = = =   — = =

— = —   — = — —

— — — — — — — — — —

Wisconsin's lakes are a fisherman's delight. Of the many game fish in Wisconsin waters, one is the state fish. Find out which one by filling in the blanks below each picture. The letters above the double lines will spell out the answer.

Wedge Wheel Puzzle

To learn how Villa Louis is described, go around the circle clockwise and copy every third letter. Put your letters in the blanks.

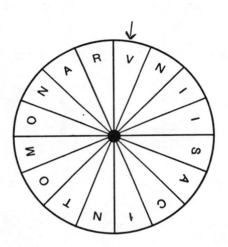

Villa Louis, a lavish _ _ _ _ _ _ _ _ _ _

_ _ _ _ _ _ _ , stands on historic ground in Wisconsin's second-oldest city, Prairie du Chien. Villa Louis has been described as one of the most authentically furnished historic houses in America - a showplace of Victorian architecture and furnishings.

Because of its tremendous output of dairy products, Wisconsin is known as "America's Dairyland". Hidden inside this milk container are 18 objects. Can you find all of them?

Mystery Word Puzzle

By placing the words from the sentence below in the appropriate spaces, two mystery words will appear in the circles.

Complete the puzzle and then fill in the mystery words.

About two hundred thousand Canada geese use Wetland Area during their fall migrations.

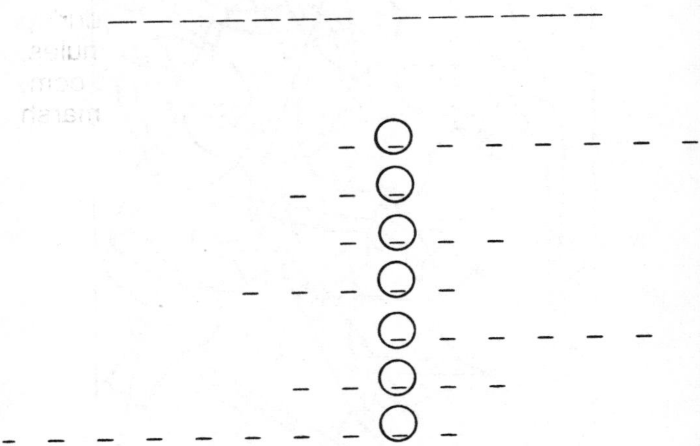

_ _ _ _ _ _ _ _   _ _ _ _ _ _

_ O _ _ _ _ _ _

_ _ O

_ O _ _

_ _ _ O _

O _ _ _ _ _

_ _ O _ _

_ _ _ _ _ _ _ _ O _

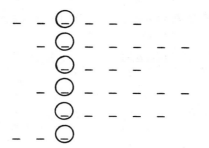

(Mallards and blue-wing teal breed here during the summer; egrets, herons, coots, gallinules, deer, muskrat and other small animals are common in this national wildlife refuge and marsh wildlife area).

PAGE 1 Answer: May 29, 1848

PAGE 2 Answer: 1. F, 2, C, 3. G, 4. E, 5. H
6. D, 7. A, 8. B

PAGE 3 Answers: 1. H, 2. F, 3. G, 4. I, 5. A,
6. E, 7. D, 8. C, 9. B

PAGE 4 Answers: 1. Potawatomi, 2. Chippewa, 3. Ottawa, 4. Dakota, 5. Winnebago,
6. Menominee, 7. Kickapoo, 8. Iowa

PAGE 5 Answers: 1. Clover, 2. Thistles,
3. Lupine, 4. Violet, 5. Trillium, 6. Bloodroot
7. Columbine, 8. Chicory, 9. Queen Anne's
Lace, 10. Jack in the Pulpit

PAGE 6 Answer: Badger

PAGE 7 Answer: Black

PAGE 8 & 9 Answers: 1. Ralph Votapek,
2. Thor Johnson, 3. George Catlin, 4. John
Curry, 5. Aaron Bohrod, 6. Edward Steichen,
7. Alfred Sessler, 8. Edna Ferber, 9. Horace
Gregory, 10. August Derluth, 11. Hamlin Garland, 12. Georgia O'Keeffe, 13. Karl Knaths,
14. Glenway Wescott, 15. George Peck, 16.
Bill Nye, 17. Ella Wilcox, 18. Laura Wilder

PAGE 10 Answer: Wisconsin leads the nation
in the making of paper.

PAGE 11 Answers: 1. Popple, 2. Willow,
3. Hemlock, 4. Spruce, 5. Pine, 6. Fir,
7. Tamarack, 8. Cedar

PAGE 12 Answer: Granite

PAGE 13 Answer: Cabbage

PAGE 14 Answer: The first house in the United States to be wired for electricity was in Appleton.

PAGE 15 Answers: 1. In the Sweet Bye and Bye, 2. The Little Brown Church in the Vale, 3. Silver Threads Among the Gold, 4. After the Ball

PAGE 16 Answers:
1. bow on boot instead of boot lace
2. hook on pole curves down instead of up
3. handkerchief in logger's pocket
4. logger's belt is different
5. different heel on logger's boot
6. lace on boot is missing
7. 4 lines on boot instead of 3
8. different design in logger's pants
9. 5 buttons on logger's shirt instead of 6
10. logger is wearing a watch
11. different moustache on logger
12. 3 buttons instead of 2 on back of logger's jacket
13. pocket on shirt is missing
14. different hat on logger in background
15. banana growing in place of cattail
16. 4 tree stumps instead of 5
17. chimney on cabin is missing

PAGE 18 Answers:

```
S   P   A   R
C   A   R   T
H   U   S   H
O   N   C   E
O   W   E   D
L   O   N   E
F   L   E   A
O   L   A   F
```

PAGE 19 Answers: 1. allowing, women, vote, 2. unemployment compensation, 3. soil, water, conservation, 4. seat belt

PAGE 20 Answers: Watermelon, Strawberries, Grapes, Tomato, Raspberries, Cherries, Plums, Pears, Apples, Gooseberry, Cranberry

PAGE 21 Answers: Mossycup Oak, Quaking Aspen, Big Tooth Aspen, Tamarack, Northern Red Oak, Hemlock, Swamp White Oak, Paper Birch, Silver Maple, River Birch

Missing Letters Will Spell - Sugar Maple

PAGE 22 Answers: Stony Hill Schoolhouse, Waubeka.

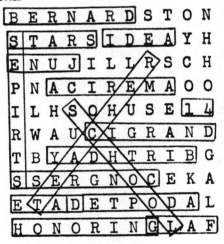

PAGE 23 Answer: Water Fluoridation to fight tooth decay.

136

PAGE 24 Answers:

TERN	FERN	T
DOVE	LOVE	D
KITE	KATE	I
PHEASANT	PLEASANT	H
WREN	WHEN	R
CRANE	CRONE	A
EIDER	RIDER	E
SWANS	SCANS	W
RAIL	PAIL	R
COOT	BOOT	C
BAIRD	LAIRD	B

BIRDWATCHER

PAGE 25 Answers: 1. C, 2. G, 3. F, 4. D, 5. H, 6. B, 7. E, 8. A

PAGE 26 Answer: La Crosse

PAGE 27 Answer: Wood Violet

PAGE 28 Answer: At one time more than one hundred circuses had headquarters in Wisconsin.

PAGE 29 (top) Answer: Houdini

```
   E  H  C  O
   |  |
   R—I  U  H
         /
   D  I  W—E
            \
   S—S—I  N
      |
      I
```

PAGE 29 (bottom) Answers: 1-D, 2-G, 3-F, 4-A, 5-C, 6-E, 7-B

PAGE 30 Answer: Green-Bay Intelligencer

PAGE 31 Answer: Margarethe Schurz

PAGE 32 Answers: Long, Poygan, Puckaway, Butternut, Chippewa, Spider, Mendota, Geneva, Green, Balsam, Chetac, Eagle, Koshkoning. Lake Winnebago - Largest of over eighty-five hundred lakes which are mapped in the state of Wisconsin.

PAGE 33 Answer: Two cars raced from Green Bay to Madison in the first auto race ever held.

PAGES 34-35 Answers: Part 1. 1-E, 2-T, 3-K, 4-P, 5-G, 6-B, 7-N, 8-D, 9-S, 10-O, 11-A, 12-L, 13-V, 14-C, 15-R, 16-F, 17-W, 18-I, 19-U, 20-M, 21-Y.
1. The Green Bay Packers Football team won the first two Super Bowl games in 1967 and 1968.
2. In 1957, the Milwaukee Braves baseball team won the world series.

```
                        F
            GAMES       O
                 I  E   O  W
            BOWL  R     T  O
            A     W  I  B  R
            Y  BASEBALL
                  U     S  L  D
            B     K     L
            R     E        T
            PACKERS        W
            V        U  WON
            TEAM     P  O
            S     GREEN
                  R
```

PAGE 36 Answer: Madison State Capital

138

PAGE 37 Answer: Solomon Juneau

PAGE 38 Answer: The oldest continuously operating radio station in the world is Radio Station WHA at Madison. The first music-appreciation program was broadcast by WHA, the first educational radio station.

PAGE 39 Answer:

```
              L
          WATER
            K  B
          EAGLE  W
         IS  A    O
             C RIVER
             H  G E L
            LAKE  R D
        T  I S Y
      CHAIN T
        O N
        U     T
        G     H
        H  THE
       TO H
        FRESH
```

TWENTY-SEVEN

PAGE 40-41 Answers: 1. The Museum of Medical Progress at Prairie du Chien exhibits depict medicine's progress in Wisconsin and the Midwest.   2. The National Railroad Museum at Green Bay preserves the history of railroading. 3. The Dard Hunter Paper Museum at Appleton displays the history of paper-making methods. 4. The country's most complete collection of guns can be seen in Madison at the museum of the State Historical Society of Wisconsin. 5. Exhibits of historic agricultural machinery and early

139

handcrafts can be seen at the State Farm and Craft Museum in Nelson Dewey State Park. 6. Rhinelander's Logging Museum has one of the most complete displays of old-time lumbering. 7. The Circus World Museum at Baraboo displays objects recalling days when Wisconsin was the leading circus state.

PAGE 42 Answer: Former Green Bay Packer Quarterback Champion, Bart Starr, is honored in the Football Hall of Fame.

PAGE 43 Answers: 1. Bailey, 2. Ira Bong, 3. Cushing

PAGE 44 Answers: 1-E, 2-G, 3-J, 4-A, 5-B, 6-I, 7-C, 8-F, 9-D, 10-H

PAGE 45 Answer: Some of the first aluminum utensils ever manufactured were produced in the state of Wisconsin.

```
              T
           M  H
          STATE
           N
           U
       W  OF
       E   A
      PRODUCED
       E   T
          O U U
          FIRST
            E EVER
            D N
            S S
      WISCONSIN
        N M   L
         THE  S
```

PAGE 46 Answer: On Wisconsin

PAGE 47 Answer: Trout

PAGE 48 Answer:

```
             P
             U  T
             R  A  G
       L  ZINC  R
       E     T  O  A
    BARITE    N  V
       D         I  E
                 TALC
          STONE     L
       L  A         A
       IRON         Y
       M  D
       E
```

PAGE 49 Answer: The first contour farming in the United States was tried near Coon Valley.

PAGE 50 Answer: It is said to be the concentrated lake region in the world.

PAGE 51 Answers: Gel, oak, leg, din, and, mix, elk, inn, rye - Golda Meir

PAGE 52 & 53 Answers: 1. different design in Indian's arm band, 2. wristband is missing, 3. branch on log is missing, 4. bottom of tomahawk handle is missing, 5. different design in Indian's waist band, 6. headband on Indian is missing, 7. butterfly on mushroom next to tree, 8. 3 cattails instead of 2, 9. end of canoe paddle is different shape, 10. 2 feathers in headband of Indian in canoe, 11. extra flower on vine around tree, 12. gun is different, 13. sleeve of robe is shorter, 14. cuff on robe sleeve is missing, 15. 4 buttons on robe instead of 3,

16. 1 canoe in background instead of 2, 17. tree in background is different, 18. leaves on bush are different shape, 19. turtle next to stump.

PAGE 54 Answers: Saxon, Unnamed, Copper, Gile, Morgan, Big Manitou, Brownstone, Power Dam.
Superior – Four of them are found in the Montreal River in Iron County.

PAGE 55 Answer: Increase Allen Lapham

```
                    W C
                    A O
                    R L
              B HUMID
              L O
        A WINTER
        U   Z   A
        T   Z   I
        U   A  SNOW
    SUMMER    P   I
    L N       D   N
    E        HAIL D
    E          N  Y
    T          G
```

PAGE 56 Answers: 1. George Van Brunt invented the first machine to scatter and bury seeds successfully. 2. John Stevens developed a roller mill to increase production of fine, white flour. 3. John Appleby invented a twine binder machine for use on reapers to bind bundles of grain automatically. 4. Both Peter Houston, Jr. and Henry Bennett created and improved photography equipment. 5. Christopher Latham Sholes, along with two other men, invented the typewriter.

PAGE 57 Answer: The House On The Rock

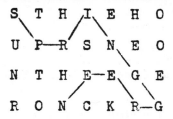

```
S   T   H   I   E   H   O

U   P—R   S   N   E   O

N   T   H   E—E   G   E

R   O   N   C   K   R—G
```

PAGE 58 Answer: Racine is thought to have the largest population of people of Danish ancestry in the United States.

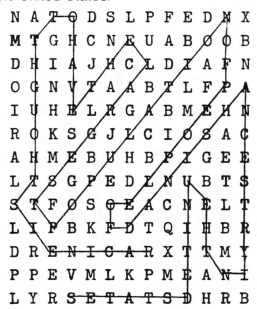

```
N   A   T   O   D   S   L   P   F   E   D   N   X
M   T   G   H   C   N   E   U   A   B   O   O   B
D   H   I   A   J   H   C   L   D   I   A   F   N
O   G   N   V   T   A   A   B   T   L   F   P   A
I   U   H   E   L   R   G   A   B   M   E   H   N
R   O   K   S   G   J   L   C   I   O   S   A   C
A   H   M   E   B   U   H   B   P   I   G   E   E
L   T   S   G   P   E   D   L   N   U   B   T   S
S   T   F   O   S   O   E   A   C   N   E   L   T
L   I   P   B   K   F   D   T   Q   I   H   B   R
D   R   E   N   I   C   A   R   X   T   T   M   Y
P   P   E   V   M   L   K   P   M   E   A   N   I
L   Y   R   S   E   T   A   T   S   D   H   R   B
```

143

PAGE 59 Answers: 1. Bob, 2. ate, 3. led, 4. tax, 5. Fa
Battle of Bad Axe

PAGE 60 Answer: Geese

PAGE 61 Answer: Frank Lloyd Wright
Taliesin

PAGE 62 Answers: 1-H, 2-I, 3-F, 4-G, 5-B, 6-C, 7-D, 8-J, 9-A, 10-K, 11-E.

PAGE 63 Answer: Door, Barron, LaCrosse, Burnett, Dunn, Buffalo, Chippewa, Green.

PAGE 64 Answer: Teacher, Lawyer, Senator, Farmer.

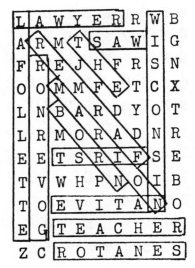

144

PAGE 65 Answer:

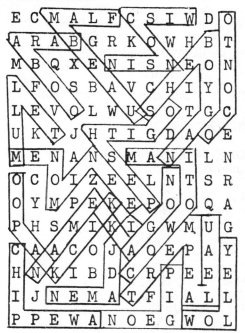

PAGE 66-67 Answers: 1. cows, 2. thin, 3. rod, 4. visit, 5. wilderness, 6. fish, 7. tribe, 8. cap, 9. traders, 10. canoe, 11. WI
The first crop said to be harvested in Wisconsin was wild rice.

PAGES 68-69 Answer: Paul Bunyan, Babe the Blue Ox.

PAGES 70-71 Answer: Fox River, Appleton

PAGE 72 Answers: 1. Ezekial Gillispie fought and won in the Wisconsin Supreme Court the right for blacks to vote in Wisconsin. 2. Al Jareau is a famous singer and recording star. 3. Black dancer, Ferne Caulker-Bronson, founded the Ko-Thi Dance Company which performs through the midwest. 4. In 1978, Barbara Nichols, became the first black to be elected president of the American Nurse's Association.

PAGE 73 Answer: The International Crane Foundation near Baraboo has the world's largest crane collection.

PAGES 74-75 Answers:

Column A	Column B
1. Pup	1. Up
2. Teen	2. Ten
3. Neat	3. Eat
4. Drip	4. Rip
5. Lead	5. Homonym is Led
6. Tear	6. Tea
7. Rove	7. Roe
8. Rain	8. Ran
9. Seat	9. Eat

P E N D A R V I S

PAGE 76 Answers: 1. B, 2. K, 3. D, 4. G, 5. J, 6. I, 7. H, 8. E, 9. F 10. C 11. A

PAGE 77 Answer: Milwaukee
1. G A T H E R I N G P L A C E
   B Y T H E W A T E R S
2. A E I A E E A E
3. A E I A E E O U
4. A E M I L K A E E O U
5. A M I L K A E E O U
6. A M I L K A E U E O
7. W M I L K A E U E O
8. W M I L K A E U E
9. M I L K A U K E E

PAGE 78 Answer: Robin

PAGE 79 Answer: Old Abe

PAGE 80 Answer: Frances Elizabeth Willard founded the World's Women's Temperence Union. After her death in 1898, a statue of her was placed in the Hall of Fame at the Capital in Washington.

PAGE 81 Answer: Wisconsin is one of the six states which made up what was once known as the Badger State because some of the lead miners burrowed into sides of hills like badgers instead of taking time to build houses.

PAGE 82 Answer: Red Granite

PAGE 83 Answer: Carrie Jacobs Bond, famous song writer.

PAGE 84 Answers: 1. Dr. William Beaumont made important discoveries concerning digestion of food. 2. Wisconsin scientist, Dr. harry Steenbock, conducted an experiment which led to the discovery that ultraviolet radiation produces vitamin D in foods. 3. Dr. Elmer V. McCollum discovered discovered Vitamins A, B, and D while doing research at the University of Wisconsin in Madison. He was assisted by Marguerite Davis.

PAGE 85 Answer: William Hoard. He is known to be the father of modern dairying.

PAGE 86 Answer: Leftover letters spell Outdoor Ethnic Museum Eagle.

```
O L A N O I T A N U
M U E S U M T I I D
S F O R T Y S S N O
N I O R D N W E E C
A N E T O H I E T I
I N C Q I S K E E N
G S S C R M S N E H
E I M M I G R A N T
W T D U S E D Y T E
R L A U M E A L H G
O U N L E D L R O W
N M E G E R M A N S
```

PAGE 87 Answer: The Cave of the Mounds.

```
TWEET
HEATH
ELITE
CHASM
ALAMO
V   U
E   N
O   D
FLOSS
```

A dynamite blast accidentally uncovered the entrance to this beautiful subterranean palace of limestone and crystal carved by seeping water over 400 million years ago. The cave, noted for its great variety of formations and unusually brilliant coloring can be seen in Blue Mounds, Wisconsin.

PAGE 88-89 Answers:

1. T H E W A E L D E R H A U S
2. T H E W A E L D E R H O U S E
3. A T H E W E L D E R H O U S E
4. A T H E H O U S E
5. A H O U S E T H E
6. A H O U S E T H E W I S C O N S I N
7. A H O U S E I N T H E W I S C O N S
8. A H O U S E I N T H E W C O N
9. A H O U S E I N T H E W O
10. A H O U S E I N T H E W O S O S
11. A H O U S E I N T H E W O O S S
12. A H O U S E I N T H E W O O D S

A House In The Woods
A replica of the John Michael Kohler home
in Austria.

PAGE 89 Answer: Sheboygan

PAGE 90 Answer: White-Tailed Deer

PAGE 91 Answer: Sugar Maple

PAGE 92-93 Answers: Part 1. 1-J, 2-O, 3-K, 4-L, 5-C, 6-M, 7-A, 8-E, 9-F, 10-P, 11-N, 12-B, 13-D, 14-I, 15-H, 16-G
Part 2. 1. medals, skating, single, Olympics.
2. holding, record, pitcher, Baseball's
3. Champion, hitter, career, 4. organized, Packers, football, 5. considered, greatest, coaches.

PAGE 94 Answers: St. Croix, Lac Court Oreilles, Lac du Flambeau, Mole Lake, Menominee, Stockbridge and Bad River are Indian Reservation in Wisconsin.

PAGE 95 Answer: Washington Island has the largest settlement of residents of Icelandic descent in the United States. The St. Croix and Lower St. Croix rivers are national rivers.

PAGE 96 Answers:
1. James A. Lovell. He became the world's most experienced spaceman yet he never landed on the moon.
2. Louis Jolliet (1645-1700)
3. Jacques Marquette (1637-1675)

PAGE 97 Answers: 1. Pew, 2. Six, 3. Me, 4. Potato, 5. Auk, 6. Bag, 7. Ox.

PAGE 98 Answer: Wisconsin's first state park is Interstate State Park. Working together, Wisconsin and Minnesota established the park which is the first state park ever to be developed by two states.

PAGE 99 Answer: Ringling Brothers Circus began.

PAGE 100-101 Answers: 1. Bear, 2. Rocky, 3. Otter, 4. Manitou, 5. Stockton, 6. Oak, 7. Sand, 8. Eagle, 9. York, 10. Raspberry, 11. Ironwood, 12. Devil's, 13. Cat, 14. Gull, 15. Outer, 16. Hermit, 17. Basswood, 18. LaPointe, 19. Long, 20. Michigan, 21. South Twin, 22. North Twin

PAGE 102 Answers:
1. Dear Miss Issippi (Mississippi), 2. Win a bagel (Winnebago), 3. Rip on Wisconsin (Ripon, Wisconsin), 4. A mini soda (Minnesota), 5. Oh Claire! (Eau Claire), 6. La, La, La, La, La-LaCrosse, LaFarge, LaValle, LaGrange, LaPointe

PAGE 103 Answer: Charles de Langlade

PAGE 104 Answer: Stagecoach Inn on the Wisconsin frontier.

```
H  T  I  M  S  K  C  A  L  B   B
S  K  T  A  G  E  C  O  H   E  E
S  E  L  R  A  H  C  S  A   N  A
C  T  D  L  O  H  U  H  I   I  U
N  T  N  O  N  B  T  O  H   A  T
E  L  W  I  N  S  I  P  C   R  I
O  E  N  E  S  I  N  N  F   O  F
R  O  E  N  T  I  E  R  S   M  U
T  R  A  V  E  L  E  R  S   O  L
G  E  S  U  O  H  E  D  A   W  N
```

PAGE 105 Answer: Ice Velocipede

```
      J  U  L     I     U  S
            S  C  H  A  E  D  M  M  E     L
            H  E  V  A  D  L  I  N  V  E
         I  N  V  E  N  T  I  I     E  E
            E  L  I  G  H  T  Y
V  E  H  I  C  L  E  W
      S  N  O  C  W  O
      W  I  S  C  O  S  O  N        I  N
      H     C  I  S  A
            P  E  A  T  E  N  T  S
            E  A  I  G  H  T  E  E  N
            D  D  A  T  E  D
            E  I  G  H  T
```

151

PAGE 106 Answer: They were Academy Award winners.

PAGE 107: Answer: Passenger Pigeons

PAGE 108 Answers: Jonathan Carver (1710-1780), Daniel Duluth (1636-1710), Jean Nicolet (1598-1642).

PAGE 109 Answers: 1. River, 2. Willow, 3. Trout, 4. Bulb, 5. Stars, 6. Eagle.

PAGE 110 Answer: Wittman Field (Oshkosh, Wisconsin)

```
            W O R L D S
          A I R C R A F T
        W I T H
      H O S T S
    M U S E U M
E X P E R I M E N T A L
A S S O C I A T I O N

      F L Y I N
    A I R
C O N V E N T I O N
      L A   G E S T
  A N D
```

PAGE 111 Answer: leftover letters spell Wisconsin Topography.

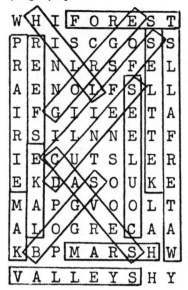

PAGE 112 Answers:

```
S M A R T
C R U S H
H I N G E
O       B
O       L
L       I
O R I O N
F R O N D
```

PAGE 113 Answer: Father Marquette

153

Circled letters unscrambled spell Milwaukee County Zoo.

```
            Y
       FLAMINGO
       I K
         R   E     B
       CHEETAH   O
       O   M   S   A
    HIPPOPOTAMUS
       P   U   E
       E   T   R
       R HORNBILL
    W  H     M
    APE ALLIGATOR
    L   A   I L
    L D   O K   S
    A SKINKS EEL
    R       N   A
    OWL     GAZELLE
            K     L
         C AMEL     K
```

PAGE 116 Answers:

Salmon	M
Sturgeon	U
Bass	S
Pike	K
Perch	E
Lake	L
Bluegill	L
Suckers	U
Rainbow	N
Tiger	G
Smelt	E

PAGE 117 Answer: New Glarus

154

PAGE 118 Answer: Father of our National Parks System.

PAGE 119 Answer: Potawatomi

PAGE 120 Answers: 1. Serf, 2. Taxi, 3. Ogre, 4. Lawn, 5. Eyed
STONEFIELD
Nelson Dewey (circled letters)

PAGE 121 Answer: Eric Heiden

PAGE 122-123 Answers: Part 1: 1-E, 2-I, 3-A, 4-Y, 5-W, 6-D, 7-F, 8-U, 9-M, 10-T, 11-S, 12-K, 13-O, 14-N, 15-L, 16-R, 17-H, 18-B, 19-C
Marathon County has more miles of marked snowmobile trails than any other area in the United States.

```
          MORE
           T     C   U
          HAS    O   IN
           E     U   I
        MARATHON    T
        A     R  T  E
        R  THAN Y   D
        K     I     S
        E  MILES    T
        D     S     A
           A        T
        SNOWMOBILE
           Y     F   S
```

```
T I M B E R W O L F
            S H R E W S
      R A B B I T
            B A T S
S Q U I R R E L
      M A R T E N
      P U M A
            F I S H E R
  B U F F A L O
      M O L E
            B A D G E R
                D E E R
W O L V E R I N E
                E L K
      C A R I B O U
```

PAGE 125 Answer: White Tailed Deer. It is believed Wisconsin is host to at least five hundred thousand of this mammal annually.

PAGE 126 Answers:

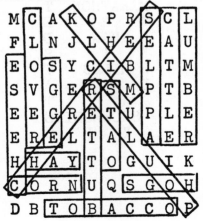

PAGE 127 Answer: Galena

PAGE 138 Answers: 1. G, 2. E, 3. F, 4. B, 5. I, 6. C, 7. D, 8. H, 9. J, 10. A

PAGE 129 Answer: Muskellunge

PAGE 130 Answer: Victorian Mansion

PAGE 131 Answer: A tulip, a crown, the letter G, an anchor, a wishbone, a bat, a loaf of bread, a duck, a ladle, a hoe, a mushroom, a fish hook, an umbrella, the letter P, a sock, a pan, a flashlight, a question mark.

PAGE 132 Answer:

```
        T H O U S A N D
    T W O
        A R E A
T H E I R
        C A N A D A
    A B O U T
M I G R A T I O N S
```

PAGE 133 Answers:

```
D U R I N G
  W E T L A N D
      F A L L
  H U N D R E D
      G E E S E
U S E
```

Horicon Refuge